Name

Address

Postcode

☎ Home

☎ Mobile

Email

In case of emergency contact:

Name

☎ Tel.

DairyDiary.co.uk

 @OriginalDairyDiary

To order: 0344 4725265

PLANNER 2023

JANUARY	FEBRUARY	MARCH
1 Sun	1 Wed	1 Wed
2 Mon BANK HOLIDAY UK	2 Thu	2 Thu
3 Tue BANK HOLIDAY SCOTLAND	3 Fri	3 Fri
4 Wed	**4 Sat**	**4 Sat**
5 Thu	**5 Sun**	**5 Sun**
6 Fri	6 Mon	6 Mon
7 Sat	7 Tue	7 Tue
8 Sun	8 Wed	8 Wed
9 Mon	9 Thu	9 Thu
10 Tue	10 Fri	10 Fri
11 Wed	**11 Sat**	**11 Sat**
12 Thu	**12 Sun**	**12 Sun**
13 Fri	13 Mon	13 Mon
14 Sat	14 Tue	14 Tue
15 Sun	15 Wed	15 Wed
16 Mon	16 Thu	16 Thu
17 Tue	17 Fri	17 Fri BANK HOLIDAY N. IRELAND
18 Wed	**18 Sat**	**18 Sat**
19 Thu	**19 Sun**	**19 Sun**
20 Fri	20 Mon	20 Mon
21 Sat	21 Tue	21 Tue
22 Sun	22 Wed	22 Wed
23 Mon	23 Thu	23 Thu
24 Tue	24 Fri	24 Fri
25 Wed	**25 Sat**	**25 Sat**
26 Thu	**26 Sun**	**26 Sun**
27 Fri	27 Mon	27 Mon
28 Sat	28 Tue	28 Tue
29 Sun		29 Wed
30 Mon		30 Thu
31 Tue		31 Fri

APRIL	MAY	JUNE
1 Sat	1 Mon BANK HOLIDAY UK	1 Thu
2 Sun	2 Tue	2 Fri
3 Mon	3 Wed	**3 Sat**
4 Tue	4 Thu	**4 Sun**
5 Wed	5 Fri	5 Mon
6 Thu	**6 Sat**	6 Tue
7 Fri BANK HOLIDAY UK	**7 Sun**	7 Wed
8 Sat	8 Mon	8 Thu
9 Sun	9 Tue	9 Fri
10 Mon BANK HOLIDAY UK (EXCL. SCOTLAND)	10 Wed	**10 Sat**
11 Tue	11 Thu	**11 Sun**
12 Wed	12 Fri	12 Mon
13 Thu	**13 Sat**	13 Tue
14 Fri	**14 Sun**	14 Wed
15 Sat	15 Mon	15 Thu
16 Sun	16 Tue	16 Fri
17 Mon	17 Wed	**17 Sat**
18 Tue	18 Thu	**18 Sun**
19 Wed	19 Fri	19 Mon
20 Thu	**20 Sat**	20 Tue
21 Fri	**21 Sun**	21 Wed
22 Sat	22 Mon	22 Thu
23 Sun	23 Tue	23 Fri
24 Mon	24 Wed	**24 Sat**
25 Tue	25 Thu	**25 Sun**
26 Wed	26 Fri	26 Mon
27 Thu	**27 Sat**	27 Tue
28 Fri	**28 Sun**	28 Wed
29 Sat	29 Mon BANK HOLIDAY UK	29 Thu
30 Sun	30 Tue	30 Fri
	31 Wed	

P.T.O. July–December 2023

JULY	AUGUST	SEPTEMBER
1 Sat	1 Tue	1 Fri
2 Sun	2 Wed	**2 Sat**
3 Mon	3 Thu	**3 Sun**
4 Tue	4 Fri	4 Mon
5 Wed	**5 Sat**	5 Tue
6 Thu	**6 Sun**	6 Wed
7 Fri	7 Mon BANK HOLIDAY SCOTLAND	7 Thu
8 Sat	8 Tue	8 Fri
9 Sun	9 Wed	**9 Sat**
10 Mon	10 Thu	**10 Sun**
11 Tue	11 Fri	11 Mon
12 Wed BANK HOLIDAY N. IRELAND	**12 Sat**	12 Tue
13 Thu	**13 Sun**	13 Wed
14 Fri	14 Mon	14 Thu
15 Sat	15 Tue	15 Fri
16 Sun	16 Wed	**16 Sat**
17 Mon	17 Thu	**17 Sun**
18 Tue	18 Fri	18 Mon
19 Wed	**19 Sat**	19 Tue
20 Thu	**20 Sun**	20 Wed
21 Fri	21 Mon	21 Thu
22 Sat	22 Tue	22 Fri
23 Sun	23 Wed	**23 Sat**
24 Mon	24 Thu	**24 Sun**
25 Tue	25 Fri	25 Mon
26 Wed	**26 Sat**	26 Tue
27 Thu	**27 Sun**	27 Wed
28 Fri	28 Mon BANK HOLIDAY UK (EXCL. SCOTLAND)	28 Thu
29 Sat	29 Tue	29 Fri
30 Sun	30 Wed	**30 Sat**
31 Mon	31 Thu	

OCTOBER	NOVEMBER	DECEMBER
1 Sun	1 Wed	1 Fri
2 Mon	2 Thu	**2 Sat**
3 Tue	3 Fri	**3 Sun**
4 Wed	**4 Sat**	4 Mon
5 Thu	**5 Sun**	5 Tue
6 Fri	6 Mon	6 Wed
7 Sat	7 Tue	7 Thu
8 Sun	8 Wed	8 Fri
9 Mon	9 Thu	**9 Sat**
10 Tue	10 Fri	**10 Sun**
11 Wed	**11 Sat**	11 Mon
12 Thu	**12 Sun**	12 Tue
13 Fri	13 Mon	13 Wed
14 Sat	14 Tue	14 Thu
15 Sun	15 Wed	15 Fri
16 Mon	16 Thu	**16 Sat**
17 Tue	17 Fri	**17 Sun**
18 Wed	**18 Sat**	18 Mon
19 Thu	**19 Sun**	19 Tue
20 Fri	20 Mon	20 Wed
21 Sat	21 Tue	21 Thu
22 Sun	22 Wed	22 Fri
23 Mon	23 Thu	**23 Sat**
24 Tue	24 Fri	**24 Sun**
25 Wed	**25 Sat**	25 Mon BANK HOLIDAY UK
26 Thu	**26 Sun**	26 Tue BANK HOLIDAY UK
27 Fri	27 Mon	27 Wed
28 Sat	28 Tue	28 Thu
29 Sun	29 Wed	29 Fri
30 Mon	30 Thu	**30 Sat**
31 Tue		**31 Sun**

Contents

USEFUL REMINDERS

PERSONAL

Bank

Beauty therapist

Building society

Citizen's Advice	citizensadvice.org.uk
for England	03444 111 444
for Wales	03444 77 20 20

Credit card emergency 1

Credit card emergency 2

Hairdresser

Life insurance policy number

☎ contact

renewal date

Samaritans	116 123 (or local branch)
	samaritans.org

Solicitor

Work

HEALTH

Blood group

Chemist

Chiropodist

Dentist

Doctor

Hospital

Medical insurance policy number

☎ contact

renewal date

National insurance number

NHS (non-emergency) 111 nhs.uk

NHS number

Optician

Notes

OME

oiler service date

hildminder/nursery

ouncil

lectrician

lectricity provider

as engineer

as provider

ome insurance policy number

☎ contact

renewal date

lumber

olice (non-emergency) 101 police.uk

chool

V licence renewal date

et

Vater provider

TRAVEL

Car insurance policy number

☎ contact

renewal date

Breakdown service

Driving licence number

Garage

MOT due date

Road tax renewal date

Service date

Vehicle registration number

National Rail enq. 0345 748 4950

nationalrail.co.uk

Taxi

Passport adviceline 0300 222 0000

gov.uk/passport-advice-line

Passport number

renewal date

EHIC/GHIC number

renewal date

Travel agent

Travel insurance policy number

☎ contact

renewal date

FAMILY & FRIENDS

Name

Address

Home

Work

Mobile

Email

Name

Address

Home

Work

Mobile

Email

Name

Address

Home

Work

Mobile

Email

Name

Address

Home

Work

Mobile

Email

Name

Address

Home

Work

Mobile

Email

Name

Address

Home

Work

Mobile

Email

Name

Address

Home

Work

Mobile

Email

Name

Address

Home

Work

Mobile

Email

Name

Address

Home

Work

Mobile

Email

Name

Address

Home

Work

Mobile

Email

Name

Address

Home

Work

Mobile

Email

Name

Address

Home

Work

Mobile

Email

Name
Address

Home
Work
Mobile
Email

Name
Address

Home
Work
Mobile
Email

Name
Address

Home
Work
Mobile
Email

Name
Address

Home
Work
Mobile
Email

Name
Address

Home
Work
Mobile
Email

Name
Address

Home
Work
Mobile
Email

Name

Address

Home

Work

Mobile

Email

Name

Address

Home

Work

Mobile

Email

Name

Address

Home

Work

Mobile

Email

Name

Address

Home

Work

Mobile

Email

Name

Address

Home

Work

Mobile

Email

Name

Address

Home

Work

Mobile

Email

HOME BUDGETING

	JANUARY	FEBRUARY	MARCH
Opening balance			
Income			
New balance			
Birthdays/Christmas			
Car insurance			
Car MOT/service/tax			
Clothing/shoes			
Council tax			
Dentist/optician			
Electricity			
Entertainment			
Gas/oil/solid fuel			
Groceries			
Hairdresser/beauty			
Holidays			
Home insurance			
Life/medical insurance			
Mobile/phone/internet			
Mortgage/rent			
Newspapers/magazines			
Petrol/fares			
Pet care/insurance			
Savings			
Subscriptions			
TV licence/satellite			
Water			
Total expenditure			
Closing balance			

	APRIL	MAY	JUNE
Opening balance			
Income			
New balance			
Birthdays/Christmas			
Car insurance			
Car MOT/service/tax			
Clothing/shoes			
Council tax			
Dentist/optician			
Electricity			
Entertainment			
Gas/oil/solid fuel			
Groceries			
Hairdresser/beauty			
Holidays			
Home insurance			
Life/medical insurance			
Mobile/phone/internet			
Mortgage/rent			
Newspapers/magazines			
Petrol/fares			
Pet care/insurance			
Savings			
Subscriptions			
TV licence/satellite			
Water			
Total expenditure			
Closing balance			

HOME BUDGETING

	JULY	AUGUST	SEPTEMBER
Opening balance			
Income			
New balance			
Birthdays/Christmas			
Car insurance			
Car MOT/service/tax			
Clothing/shoes			
Council tax			
Dentist/optician			
Electricity			
Entertainment			
Gas/oil/solid fuel			
Groceries			
Hairdresser/beauty			
Holidays			
Home insurance			
Life/medical insurance			
Mobile/phone/internet			
Mortgage/rent			
Newspapers/magazines			
Petrol/fares			
Pet care/insurance			
Savings			
Subscriptions			
TV licence/satellite			
Water			
Total expenditure			
Closing balance			

	OCTOBER	NOVEMBER	DECEMBER
Opening balance			
Income			
New balance			
Birthdays/Christmas			
Car insurance			
Car MOT/service/tax			
Clothing/shoes			
Council tax			
Dentist/optician			
Electricity			
Entertainment			
Gas/oil/solid fuel			
Groceries			
Hairdresser/beauty			
Holidays			
Home insurance			
Life/medical insurance			
Mobile/phone/internet			
Mortgage/rent			
Newspapers/magazines			
Petrol/fares			
Pet care/insurance			
Savings			
Subscriptions			
TV licence/satellite			
Water			
Total expenditure			
Closing balance			

2022

January

Mon		3	10	17	24	31
Tue		4	11	18	25	
Wed		5	12	19	26	
Thu		6	13	20	27	
Fri		7	14	21	28	
Sat	1	8	15	22	29	
Sun	2	9	16	23	30	

February

Mon		7	14	21	28
Tue	1	8	15	22	
Wed	2	9	16	23	
Thu	3	10	17	24	
Fri	4	11	18	25	
Sat	5	12	19	26	
Sun	6	13	20	27	

March

Mon		7	14	21	28
Tue	1	8	15	22	29
Wed	2	9	16	23	30
Thu	3	10	17	24	31
Fri	4	11	18	25	
Sat	5	12	19	26	
Sun	6	13	20	27	

April

Mon		4	11	18	25
Tue		5	12	19	26
Wed		6	13	20	27
Thu		7	14	21	28
Fri	1	8	15	22	29
Sat	2	9	16	23	30
Sun	3	10	17	24	

May

Mon		2	9	16	23	30
Tue		3	10	17	24	31
Wed		4	11	18	25	
Thu		5	12	19	26	
Fri		6	13	20	27	
Sat		7	14	21	28	
Sun	1	8	15	22	29	

June

Mon		6	13	20	27
Tue		7	14	21	28
Wed	1	8	15	22	29
Thu	2	9	16	23	30
Fri	3	10	17	24	
Sat	4	11	18	25	
Sun	5	12	19	26	

July

Mon		4	11	18	25
Tue		5	12	19	26
Wed		6	13	20	27
Thu		7	14	21	28
Fri	1	8	15	22	29
Sat	2	9	16	23	30
Sun	3	10	17	24	31

August

Mon	1	8	15	22	29
Tue	2	9	16	23	30
Wed	3	10	17	24	31
Thu	4	11	18	25	
Fri	5	12	19	26	
Sat	6	13	20	27	
Sun	7	14	21	28	

September

Mon		5	12	19	26
Tue		6	13	20	27
Wed		7	14	21	28
Thu	1	8	15	22	29
Fri	2	9	16	23	30
Sat	3	10	17	24	
Sun	4	11	18	25	

October

Mon		3	10	17	24	31
Tue		4	11	18	25	
Wed		5	12	19	26	
Thu		6	13	20	27	
Fri		7	14	21	28	
Sat	1	8	15	22	29	
Sun	2	9	16	23	30	

November

Mon		7	14	21	28
Tue	1	8	15	22	29
Wed	2	9	16	23	30
Thu	3	10	17	24	
Fri	4	11	18	25	
Sat	5	12	19	26	
Sun	6	13	20	27	

December

Mon		5	12	19	26
Tue		6	13	20	27
Wed		7	14	21	28
Thu	1	8	15	22	29
Fri	2	9	16	23	30
Sat	3	10	17	24	31
Sun	4	11	18	25	

2024

January

Mon	1	8	15	22	29
Tue	2	9	16	23	30
Wed	3	10	17	24	31
Thu	4	11	18	25	
Fri	5	12	19	26	
Sat	6	13	20	27	
Sun	7	14	21	28	

February

Mon		5	12	19	26
Tue		6	13	20	27
Wed		7	14	21	28
Thu	1	8	15	22	29
Fri	2	9	16	23	
Sat	3	10	17	24	
Sun	4	11	18	25	

March

Mon		4	11	18	25
Tue		5	12	19	26
Wed		6	13	20	27
Thu		7	14	21	28
Fri	1	8	15	22	29
Sat	2	9	16	23	30
Sun	3	10	17	24	31

April

Mon	1	8	15	22	29
Tue	2	9	16	23	30
Wed	3	10	17	24	
Thu	4	11	18	25	
Fri	5	12	19	26	
Sat	6	13	20	27	
Sun	7	14	21	28	

May

Mon		6	13	20	27
Tue		7	14	21	28
Wed	1	8	15	22	29
Thu	2	9	16	23	30
Fri	3	10	17	24	31
Sat	4	11	18	25	
Sun	5	12	19	26	

June

Mon		3	10	17	24
Tue		4	11	18	25
Wed		5	12	19	26
Thu		6	13	20	27
Fri		7	14	21	28
Sat	1	8	15	22	29
Sun	2	9	16	23	30

July

Mon	1	8	15	22	29
Tue	2	9	16	23	30
Wed	3	10	17	24	31
Thu	4	11	18	25	
Fri	5	12	19	26	
Sat	6	13	20	27	
Sun	7	14	21	28	

August

Mon		5	12	19	26
Tue		6	13	20	27
Wed		7	14	21	28
Thu	1	8	15	22	29
Fri	2	9	16	23	30
Sat	3	10	17	24	31
Sun	4	11	18	25	

September

Mon		2	9	16	23	30
Tue		3	10	17	24	
Wed		4	11	18	25	
Thu		5	12	19	26	
Fri		6	13	20	27	
Sat		7	14	21	28	
Sun	1	8	15	22	29	

October

Mon		7	14	21	28
Tue	1	8	15	22	29
Wed	2	9	16	23	30
Thu	3	10	17	24	31
Fri	4	11	18	25	
Sat	5	12	19	26	
Sun	6	13	20	27	

November

Mon		4	11	18	25
Tue		5	12	19	26
Wed		6	13	20	27
Thu		7	14	21	28
Fri	1	8	15	22	29
Sat	2	9	16	23	30
Sun	3	10	17	24	

December

Mon		2	9	16	23	30
Tue		3	10	17	24	31
Wed		4	11	18	25	
Thu		5	12	19	26	
Fri		6	13	20	27	
Sat		7	14	21	28	
Sun	1	8	15	22	29	

2023

JANUARY

Mon		2	9	16	23	30
Tue		3	10	17	24	31
Wed		4	11	18	25	
Thu		5	12	19	26	
Fri		6	13	20	27	
Sat		7	14	21	28	
Sun	1	8	15	22	29	

FEBRUARY

Mon		6	13	20	27
Tue		7	14	21	28
Wed	1	8	15	22	
Thu	2	9	16	23	
Fri	3	10	17	24	
Sat	4	11	18	25	
Sun	5	12	19	26	

MARCH

Mon		6	13	20	27
Tue		7	14	21	28
Wed	1	8	15	22	29
Thu	2	9	16	23	30
Fri	3	10	17	24	31
Sat	4	11	18	25	
Sun	5	12	19	26	

APRIL

Mon		3	10	17	24
Tue		4	11	18	25
Wed		5	12	19	26
Thu		6	13	20	27
Fri		7	14	21	28
Sat	1	8	15	22	29
Sun	2	9	16	23	30

MAY

Mon	1	8	15	22	29
Tue	2	9	16	23	30
Wed	3	10	17	24	31
Thu	4	11	18	25	
Fri	5	12	19	26	
Sat	6	13	20	27	
Sun	7	14	21	28	

JUNE

Mon		5	12	19	26
Tue		6	13	20	27
Wed		7	14	21	28
Thu	1	8	15	22	29
Fri	2	9	16	23	30
Sat	3	10	17	24	
Sun	4	11	18	25	

JULY

Mon		3	10	17	24	31
Tue		4	11	18	25	
Wed		5	12	19	26	
Thu		6	13	20	27	
Fri		7	14	21	28	
Sat	1	8	15	22	29	
Sun	2	9	16	23	30	

AUGUST

Mon		7	14	21	28
Tue	1	8	15	22	29
Wed	2	9	16	23	30
Thu	3	10	17	24	31
Fri	4	11	18	25	
Sat	5	12	19	26	
Sun	6	13	20	27	

SEPTEMBER

Mon		4	11	18	25
Tue		5	12	19	26
Wed		6	13	20	27
Thu		7	14	21	28
Fri	1	8	15	22	29
Sat	2	9	16	23	30
Sun	3	10	17	24	

OCTOBER

Mon		2	9	16	23	30
Tue		3	10	17	24	31
Wed		4	11	18	25	
Thu		5	12	19	26	
Fri		6	13	20	27	
Sat		7	14	21	28	
Sun	1	8	15	22	29	

NOVEMBER

Mon		6	13	20	27
Tue		7	14	21	28
Wed	1	8	15	22	29
Thu	2	9	16	23	30
Fri	3	10	17	24	
Sat	4	11	18	25	
Sun	5	12	19	26	

DECEMBER

Mon		4	11	18	25
Tue		5	12	19	26
Wed		6	13	20	27
Thu		7	14	21	28
Fri	1	8	15	22	29
Sat	2	9	16	23	30
Sun	3	10	17	24	31

Calendar dates

UK HOLIDAYS †	2023	2024
New Year	Jan 2*	Jan 1
New Year (Scotland)	Jan 2/3*	Jan 1/2
St Patrick's Day (Northern Ireland)	Mar 17	Mar 18
Good Friday	Apr 7	Mar 29
Easter Monday	Apr 10	Apr 1
Early Spring	May 1	May 6
Spring	May 29	May 27
Battle of the Boyne (Northern Ireland)	Jul 12	Jul 12
Summer (Scotland)	Aug 7	Aug 5
Summer (except Scotland)	Aug 28	Aug 26
Christmas Day	Dec 25	Dec 25
Boxing Day	Dec 26	Dec 26

NOTABLE DATES	2023
Chinese New Year – Year of the Rabbit	Jan 22
Burns Night	Jan 25
Holocaust Memorial Day	Jan 27
Accession of Queen Elizabeth II	Feb 6
St Valentine's Day	Feb 14
Shrove Tuesday (Pancake Day)	Feb 21
St David's Day (Wales)	Mar 1
Commonwealth Day	Mar 13
St Patrick's Day (Ireland)	Mar 17
Mothering Sunday	Mar 19
International Day of Forests	Mar 21
St George's Day (England)	Apr 23
World Red Cross/Red Crescent Day	May 8
Coronation Day	Jun 2
Father's Day	Jun 18
Armed Forces' Day	Jun 24
St Swithin's Day	Jul 15
International Day of Peace	Sep 21
United Nations Day	Oct 24
Halloween	Oct 31
Armistice Day	Nov 11
Remembrance Sunday	Nov 12
St Andrew's Day (Scotland)	Nov 30

RELIGIOUS DATES

Christian

Epiphany	Jan 6
Ash Wednesday	Feb 22
Palm Sunday	Apr 2
Good Friday	Apr 7
Easter Day	Apr 9
Ascension Day, Holy Thursday	May 18
Whit Sunday, Pentecost	May 28
Trinity Sunday	Jun 4
Corpus Christi	Jun 8
Advent Sunday	Dec 3
Christmas Day	Dec 25

Buddhist

Parinirvana Day	Feb 15
Wesak (Buddha Day)	May 5
Bodhi Day (Buddha's enlightenment)	Dec 8

Hindu

Maha Shivaratri	Feb 18
Holi	Mar 7
Navaratri begins	Oct 15
Diwali begins (also celebrated by Sikhs)	Nov 12

Islamic

Ramadan begins	Mar 23
Eid Ul-Fitr	Apr 21
Eid Ul-Adha	Jun 28
Al-Hijra (New Year)	Jul 19
Milad un Nabi (Prophet's birthday)	Sep 26

Jewish

Purim begins	Mar 6
Pesach (Passover) begins	Apr 6
Shavuot (Pentecost) begins	May 26
Rosh Hashanah (Jewish New Year)	Sep 16
Yom Kippur (Day of Atonement)	Sep 25
Succoth (Tabernacles) begins	Sep 30
Chanukah begins	Dec 7

Sikh

These dates follow the Nanakshahi calendar

Birthday of Guru Gobind Singh	Jan 5
Vaisakhi	Apr 14
Martyrdom of Guru Arjan Dev	Jun 16
Martyrdom of Guru Tegh Bahadur	Nov 24
Birthday of Guru Nanak	Nov 27

Note: Many religious dates are based on the lunar calendar and, therefore, we cannot guarantee their accuracy.

†Bank Holiday dates can change
*Substitute Bank Holidays (when the date falls on a Saturday or Sunday)

PHASES OF THE MOON

● New moon

	Day	H:M
Jan	21	20:53
Feb	20	07:06
Mar	21	17:23
Apr	20	04:13
May	19	15:53
Jun	18	04:37
Jul	17	18:32
Aug	16	09:38
Sep	15	01:40
Oct	14	17:55
Nov	13	09:27
Dec	12	23:32

) First quarter

	Day	H:M
Jan	28	15:19
Feb	27	08:06
Mar	29	02:32
Apr	27	21:20
May	27	15:22
Jun	26	07:50
Jul	25	22:07
Aug	24	09:57
Sep	22	19:32
Oct	22	03:29
Nov	20	10:50
Dec	19	18:39

○ Full moon

	Day	H:M
Jan	6	23:08
Feb	5	18:29
Mar	7	12:40
Apr	6	04:35
May	5	17:34
Jun	4	03:42
Jul	3	11:39
Aug	1	18:32
Aug	31	01:36
Sep	29	09:58
Oct	28	20:24
Nov	27	09:16
Dec	27	00:33

(Last quarter

	Day	H:M
Jan	15	02:10
Feb	13	16:01
Mar	15	02:08
Apr	13	09:11
May	12	14:28
Jun	10	19:31
Jul	10	01:48
Aug	8	10:28
Sep	6	22:21
Oct	6	13:48
Nov	5	08:37
Dec	5	05:49

BRITISH SUMMERTIME (t.b.c. by Government)

▶ Clocks go forward
1 hour at 1am on
26 March

◀ Clocks go back
1 hour at 2am on
29 October

SEASONS

	Month	Day	H:M
Vernal equinox Spring begins	Mar	20	21:24
Summer solstice Summer begins	June	21	14:58
Autumnal equinox Autumn begins	Sep	23	06:50
Winter solstice Winter begins	Dec	22	03:27

WEBSITES

gov.uk/bank-holidays
when-is.com

SUNRISE AND SUNSET TIMES

Note: times vary – these are for London

Day	Rise H:M	Set H:M	Day	Rise H:M	Set H:M	Day	Rise H:M	Set H:M	Day	Rise H:M	Set H:M
January			**February**			**March**			**April**		
07	08:05	16:09	07	07:30	17:01	07	06:33	17:51	07	06:23	19:43
14	08:01	16:19	14	07:17	17:13	14	06:18	18:03	14	06:08	19:55
21	07:54	16:30	21	07:03	17:26	21	06:02	18:15	21	05:53	20:07
28	07:45	16:42	28	06:49	17:39	28	06:46	19:27	28	05:39	20:19
May			**June**			**July**			**August**		
07	05:22	20:33	07	04:45	21:14	07	04:52	21:18	07	05:33	20:39
14	05:11	20:44	14	04:43	21:19	14	05:00	21:13	14	05:44	20:26
21	05:01	20:54	21	04:43	21:22	21	05:08	21:05	21	05:55	20:12
28	04:53	21:04	28	04:46	21:22	28	05:18	20:55	28	06:06	19:57
September			**October**			**November**			**December**		
07	06:22	19:34	07	07:11	18:26	07	07:04	16:24	07	07:51	15:52
14	06:33	19:18	14	07:22	18:10	14	07:16	16:13	14	07:59	15:52
21	06:45	19:02	21	07:34	17:56	21	07:28	16:04	21	08:04	15:53
28	06:56	18:46	28	07:47	17:42	28	07:39	15:57	28	08:06	15:58

Anniversaries

GENOMES PROJECT COMPLETED

5 years

Completed in 2018, the 100,000 Genomes Project was a revolutionary gene sequencing programme and the world's largest ever project of its kind.

The project involved 85,000 participants, 1,500 NHS staff and 3,000 researchers, and was launched by then-Prime Minister David Cameron in 2012. The human genome is the blueprint that makes us who we are, and can provide clues about how vulnerable we are to certain conditions like heart disease, cancer or extremely rare genetic syndromes.

The gene sequencing undertaken allowed 1 in 4 participants with a rare illness to receive a diagnosis for the first time and has already contributed to cancer research and tailored treatment for patients.

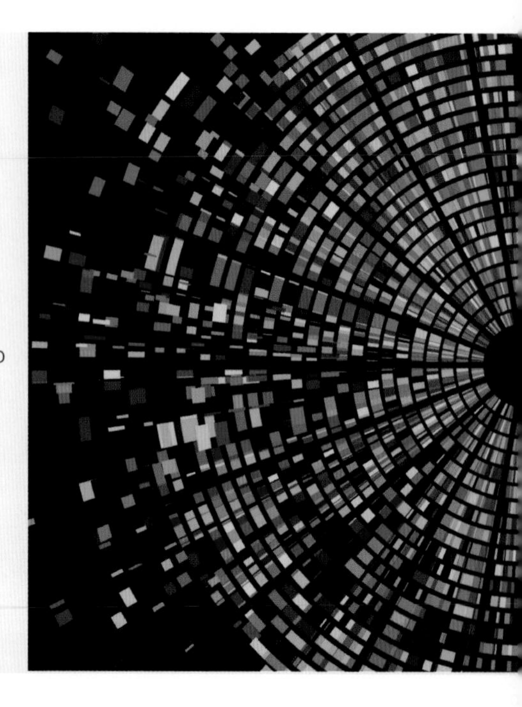

2023 MILESTONES/ANNIVERSARIES

5: The 100,000 Genomes Project is completed by scientists in Cambridge (5 December 2018)
10: Nelson Mandela dies at the age of 95 (5 December 2013)
20: Concorde makes its last ever flight from Heathrow Airport in London to Bristol Filton Airport (26 November 2003)
25: The Good Friday Agreement is signed, ending the Troubles in Northern Ireland (10 April 1998)
30: Buckingham Palace opens to the public for the first time (29 April 1993)
50: The Sydney Opera House is opened by Queen Elizabeth II (20 October 1973)
50: Concorde makes its first non-stop crossing of the Atlantic in record-breaking time 50 years ago (26 September 1973)
50: The first cohort of students graduate from distance learning institute The Open University (11 January 1973)
60: Screening of the first ever episode of *Doctor Who* on the BBC (23 November 1963)
70: The coronation of Queen Elizabeth II, who is crowned Queen of the United Kingdom, Canada, Australia, New Zealand and Her Other Realms and Territories & Head of the Commonwealth (2 June 1953)
70: The first James Bond novel *Casino Royale*, by Ian Fleming, is published (13 April 1953)
75: The Summer Olympics open in London, after a 12-year break due to WWII (29 July 1948)
100: The chimes of Big Ben are broadcast on the radio for the first time by the BBC, heralding the New Year (31 December 1923)
100: The first edition of the *Radio Times* hits newsstands (28 September 1923)
110: The first known crossword puzzle ever published appears in the US newspaper, the *New York World*. It was the invention of British-born Arthur Wynne (21 December 1913)
125: The first solo round-the-world sailing voyage, lasting 3 years, is completed by Canadian Joshua Slocum (27 June 1898)
175: Waterloo Station opens in London (11 July 1848)
250: Captain James Cook and crew become the first Europeans to sail below the Antarctic Circle (17 January 1773)

CONCORDE'S LAST COMMERCIAL FLIGHT

20 years

To many today the thought of flying from London to New York in under three hours sounds like something out of a futuristic novel.

But, of course, Concorde is in fact a technical marvel of the past – the supersonic jet took its final commercial passenger flight on 24 October 2003.

This Franco-British project began the first scheduled supersonic passenger service in 1976. Travelling at 1,350 miles per hour, this sleek miracle of aerodynamic engineering became an icon of luxury and efficiency. Following a fatal crash in 2000, ticket sales slowed and the fleet was retired in 2003.

OPENING OF THE SYDNEY OPERA HOUSE

50 years

Its iconic white points, designed to mimic the sails of a ship, are a sight that once seen can never be forgotten. And this year it is fifty years since Sydney Opera House was officially opened by Queen Elizabeth II in October 1973.

The striking design is the work of Danish architect Jørn Utzon, whose drawings were chosen from 233 entries submitted for the Opera House international design competition in 1956. Although construction was expected to last four years, it ended up taking fourteen and involved 10,000 labourers. When symphony orchestras are performing, the temperature must be kept at a constant 22.5°C to ensure the instruments stay in tune – this is achieved using seawater taken from the harbour, which circulates through the building's 22 miles (35 kilometres) of pipes!

Today more than 1.2 million audience members each year enjoy musical and other cultural performances hosted at the Sydney Opera House. The building was added to UNESCO's World Heritage List in 2007.

ANNIVERSARY & BIRTHDAY GIFT RECORD

WEDDINGS

1	Paper	14	Ivory
2	Cotton	15	Crystal
3	Leather	20	China
4	Books	25	Silver
5	Wood	30	Pearl
6	Iron	35	Coral
7	Wool	40	Ruby
8	Bronze	45	Sapphire
9	Copper	50	Gold
10	Tin	55	Emerald
11	Steel	60	Diamond
12	Silk or linen	65	Blue Sapphire
13	Lace	70	Platinum

BIRTHSTONES AND FLOWERS

Month	**Birthstone**	**Flower**
January	Garnet	Carnation
February	Amethyst	Violet
March	Aquamarine	Jonquil
April	Diamond	Sweet Pea
May	Emerald	Lily of the Valley
June	Pearl	Rose
July	Ruby	Larkspur
August	Peridot	Gladiolus
September	Sapphire	Aster
October	Opal	Calendula
November	Topaz	Chrysanthemum
December	Turquoise	Narcissus

Name	Date	Ideas	Bought	Cost

ame	Date	Ideas	Bought	Cost

Floral spring knit

This project is full of the joys of the new season and features four pretty blooms, plus leaves

Designer Lucinda Ganderton has used the finished flowers to adorn a wicker wreath, which makes a marvellous springtime decoration. You could add them to cushions, scarves or bags, or even add a brooch back to make a pretty corsage.

Measurements & sizes:
Wreath: 35cm wide
Daffodil: 10cm wide
Five-petalled flower: 8cm wide
Eight-petalled flower: 8cm wide
Rosebud: 8cm long
Large leaf: 7cm long
Small leaf: 5cm long

What you will need:
Yarn: DK yarn in shades
(A) White, (B) Yellow,
(C) Pale Green, (D) Mid Green, (E) Turquoise,
(F) Bright Pink, (G) Pale Pink, (H) Purple,
small amounts of each
Needles: 4mm
Buttons: white shank, six
Twig garland: 35cm wide
Glue gun
Tapestry needle
Tension: 20 sts x 28 rows in stocking stitch over a 10cm square using 4mm needles

Experiment with different yarn weights and their corresponding needle size to make bigger and smaller blooms for your wreath.

For an explanation of the knitting abbreviations used in this pattern please visit the website *letsknit.co.uk/knitting-abbreviations*

Begin knitting here:

DAFFODIL Make two using yarns A and B, and one in yarn B only.

Petals Make six. Using 4mm needles and yarns A or B, cast on three sts
Row 1: k to end
Row 2 and all WS rows: p to end
Row 3: (k1, m1) twice, k1. Five sts
Row 5: k2, m1, k1, m1, k2. Seven sts
Row 7: k3, m1, k1, m1, k3. Nine sts
Row 9: k1, ssk, k3, k2tog, k1. Seven sts
Row 11: k1, ssk, k1, k2tog, k1. Five sts
Row 13: k1, sl 1 kwise, k2tog, psso, k1. Three sts
Row 14: sl 1 pwise, p2tog, psso. One st
Fasten off

Trumpet Make three.
Using 4mm needles and yarn B, cast on 16 sts
Rows 1-6: (k1, p1) to end
Row 7: (k1, yfwd) to last st, k1. 31 sts
Cast off
Stitch three petals together at bottom edges to form a triangular shape. Repeat with other three petals and place one centrally on top of the other and stitch together at centre. Join the side edges of trumpet and sew cast-on edge to centre of petals

EIGHT-PETALLED FLOWER
Make two in yarn F and one in yarn G.
Using 4mm needles, cast on seven sts
Row 1: k5, turn
Row 2: k to end
Row 3: k3, turn
Row 4: k to end
Row 5: k6, turn
Row 6: k to end
Row 7: cast off five sts, k to end. Two sts
Row 8: k2, turn
Row 9: cast on five sts. Seven sts
Rep Rows 1-9 six times more, then rep Rows 1-6 once more
Cast off
Sew inside corners of first and last petals together, then arrange petals in a flower shape. Stitch them together securely at the base, then sew a button to the centre

ROSEBUD Make three. Using 4mm needles and yarn F, cast on 20 sts
Row 1: k to end
Join in yarn G
Row 2: p to end
Rows 3-6: cont in st st
Row 7: (k2tog) to end. Ten sts
Row 8: (p2tog) to end. Five sts
Join in yarn C
Rows 9-18: beg with a k row, work in st st
Cut yarn, thread through rem sts, pull tight and fasten off
Sew sides of stalk together, then roll up top section to make bud

FIVE-PETALLED FLOWER
Make two.
Petals Make five.
Using 4mm needles and yarn H, cast on four sts
Row 1: k1, (kfb) twice, k1. Six sts
Row 2 and all WS rows: p to end
Row 3: k1, kfb, k2, kfb, k1. Eight sts
Row 5: k1, kfb, k4, kfb, k1. Ten sts
Row 7: (ssk) twice, k2, (k2tog) twice. Six sts
Row 9: ssk, (k2tog) twice. Three sts
Row 10: sl 1 pwise, p2tog, psso. One st
Fasten off
Weave in ends. Sew the five petals together at the base, pleating each one to cup it slightly. Fasten off securely and sew a button to the centre

LEAVES
Large leaf Make three each in yarns C and D, and two in yarn E.
Using 4mm needles, cast on three sts
Row 1: k to end
Row 2: k1, p1, k1
Row 3: (k1, m1) twice, k1. Five sts
Row 4: k2, p1, k2
Row 5: k2, m1, k1, m1, k2. Seven sts
Row 6: k3, p1, k3
Row 7: k3, m1, k1, m1, k3. Nine sts
Row 8: k4, p1, k4
Row 9: k4, m1, k1, m1, k4. 11 sts
Row 10: k5, p1, k5
Row 11: k5, m1, k1, m1, k5. 13 sts
Row 12: k6, p1, k6
Rows 13-14: k to end
Row 15: k to last two sts, k2tog. 12 sts
Rep last row until two sts rem
Next row: k2tog. One st
Fasten off

Small leaf Make three each in yarns C and D and four in yarn E.
Work Rows 1-8 as for Large leaf. Nine sts
Row 9: k to last two sts, k2tog. Seven sts
Rep last row until two sts rem
Next row: k2tog. One st
Fasten off

To make up wreath:
Arrange flowers and leaves on garland and fix in place with a glue gun.

Everlasting flowers

Think beyond the dust and chintz: dried flowers are no longer the preserve of cemeteries or bowls of pot pourri. Seen with fresh eyes, preserved bouquets can bring texture, elegance and beauty to your home, even in the depths of winter...

There are plenty of reasons why dried flowers are suddenly so on trend, and an increasingly common sight at weddings and restaurants. Dried bouquets make a simple but structural statement and last for far longer than a conventional bunch of blooms. In fact, dried properly, a bouquet of 'everlastings', as they are sometimes called, can last for a year before needing to be replaced.

This also makes dried flowers easier on the environment than conventional flowers, which are often flown in from abroad and require immense amounts of water during the growing process. Buying a bunch of fresh flowers can be expensive and is not always eco-friendly, but dried posies come with none of these disadvantages. Yet they still offer a welcome boost of floral joy, especially during the long, cold months of winter.

USE WHAT YOU HAVE

If you have outdoor space, looking at the plants you have with fresh eyes might throw up some obvious options for drying. Hydrangeas, found in many a British back garden, are perfect for drying. So are lavender, larkspur, lady's mantle, eucalyptus and fluffy baby's breath (also known as *Gypsophila paniculata*). You can also forage for foliage to dry when out and about – wild ferns and teasels are especially well-suited to drying.

DRY IT YOURSELF

There are several different methods for drying flowers, though arguably none is easier than air drying (see instructions below).

You can also use dry evaporation, which lets you enjoy the beauty of the flowers as they dry. To do this, remove any undesired leaves, put your flowers in a vase, and add enough water so that the ends of the stems are submerged. Display on your mantelpiece and then bide your time – after two weeks, the flowers should be fully dried. This method works well for roses, hydrangeas and baby's breath.

THE BEST FLOWERS FOR DRYING

As a rule, the best plant material to choose for drying has a low moisture content and woody stems – think delphiniums rather than daisies. Some of the best options are astrantia, strawflowers, nigella, poppies, scabious and statice. Grasses, like pampas and hare's tail, also work particularly well.

Flowers with a strong structure are perfect because they will continue to hold their form when dried. Spring alliums can be left to dry naturally in the sun and picked in the summer; they'll last in a vase for months and have a dramatic, architectural feel. With a similar appearance, echinops (globe thistle) works very well. Honesty seed pods are also a natural choice and add a dash of luxury to any arrangement with their lustrous silvery shine.

While they are beautiful fresh, large, blousy flowers with many layers, such as peonies and dahlias, do not dry as well due to their high water content. However, if these are among your favourite flowers and you wish to preserve them, individual petals can still be collected and dried.

The best way to see what works is to give it a go. Picking flowers from your own garden or those found while out on a walk means you have little to lose, and it's easy to learn with practice which blooms dry best.

A WORLD OF FLORAL POSSIBILITIES

Once your flowers have dried, what next? Wreaths, pressed flowers, framed displays, bouquets, garlands – the world of everlasting flowers is your oyster.

Pressing small flowers the old-fashioned way, between the pages of a heavy hardback book, is a simple and satisfying way to dry out flowers for use on cards and for decoration. Petite posies of violas, violets, sweet peas and forget-me-nots are very good options.

When making dried flower arrangements, pay attention to tones and textures. Mixing grasses with more solid blooms will give a bouquet interest and flow. You can also experiment with colour – the deep blues of lavender contrast beautifully with the golden tones of dried grasses. Whatever you decide, everlasting flowers bring elegance and vintage style to a home, and allow us to enjoy the riches of spring and summer all year round.

HOW TO AIR-DRY A BOUQUET

You will need:
A bunch of flowers
String
A warm, dry, dark spot

Air drying is the traditional method for drying bouquets, and as luck would have it, it is also the easiest method to try at home.

1 Strip away any unwanted or excess foliage from the stems of your flowers.
2 Arrange the bouquet to your preference and tie the stems together firmly with string. The stems will shrink as they dry so make sure you have tied the string tightly enough without crushing the stalks.
3 Hang the bouquet upside down in a well-ventilated room, cupboard or garage. Rooms with high moisture levels, like bathrooms, should be avoided, but an airing cupboard is ideal. Light will bleach the flowers, so unless that's the look you're aiming for, choose somewhere dark.
4 Leave for at least three weeks until the flowers have shrunk and lost some colour. Leaving for longer won't hurt either. Be careful when handling the flowers, as they will be delicate and brittle.

Come on in, the water's lovely

Dipping into a refreshing lido on a hot summer's day. Feeling the gentle roll of the waves as you paddle in the shallows. Or simply the everyday joy of laps at your local leisure centre. Swimming, however you do it, is great for both body and mind.

And swimming really offers something for everyone, being as suitable for the aspiring athletes among us as the injured and inactive. As a mostly solitary sport, you can go at your own pace, which makes it perfect for beginners and veterans alike. And the country seems to agree: an estimated 14 million adults take a dip each year, according to Swim England.

MANY BENEFITS

The mental and physical rewards of swimming are myriad, and they aren't limited to how fit or active you are. Almost everyone can enjoy the benefits of a dip in the pool. Swimming has been shown to boost our moods, keep the body's muscles and joints healthy, and reduce the risk of developing a chronic illness. It also improves our lung function and can burn between 300 and 600 calories an hour, depending on your speed!

One of the best things about swimming? It's classed as low-impact exercise. That means it's gentle on the joints, especially when compared to running or cycling. It also makes it the perfect choice of exercise for those who may have joint problems, mobility issues or an injury.

Swimming by its very nature also takes you outside of your environment, blurring your senses and encouraging a kind of mindfulness as a result. The sounds of water have been found to boost alpha waves in the brain, which are linked to feelings of relaxation and creativity. Taking a dip also releases endorphins, the body's feel-good hormones, and therefore helps to lessen the impact of stress.

THE SWIMMING STORY

Many of us grew up going to the local leisure centre or trekking to school swimming lessons with kit bags slung over our shoulders, but swimming has a long history that dates back far beyond the school days of anyone alive today. Recreational swimming dates back to at least the Stone Age, and there are references to this form of water-based exercise in ancient literature and religious texts, including *The Odyssey*, the Bible and the Quran.

It was on chilly English shores that swimming as a competitive sport emerged for the first time. The first indoor swimming pool – likely to counter the brisk weather outdoors – opened in 1829 in Liverpool. Fewer than ten years later, the National Swimming Society had launched regular swimming galas around London. The sport first featured on the Olympic Games schedule in 1896 and has been part of the programme ever since.

Sea swimming came into fashion during the 18th century, at resorts on the South Coast like Weymouth and Torquay. The rapid growth of the railways in Victorian times opened up these resorts to visitors from around the UK and contributed to the rise of sea swimming as a leisure activity.

NEVER TOO LATE TO START

Not being able to swim is more common than you might imagine. Luckily, it is never too late to learn. Most local leisure centres cater to adult beginners as well as children and you'll find a variety of classes to suit your needs, whether that's women-only sessions, parent-and-child groups or lessons at different age groups. Individual lessons are also on offer if you'd like personalised support.

Once you've built up your confidence in the water, a whole new world of activities will open up to you. Aqua aerobics, deep water aerobics, aqua jogging, aqua circuits... That's not to mention the possibility of looking into activities like paddleboarding, kayaking and outdoor swimming at your local outdoor water park or recreational lake if you've caught the swimming bug!

THE RISE OF WILD SWIMMING

Wild swimming – taking a dip outside in lakes, rivers or the sea – also continues to grow in popularity. According to Swim England, 2.1m people across the UK say they regularly swim in open water. Many of these hardy swimmers cite the anecdotal benefits they experience as the driving factor behind their cold water adventures. Swimming outdoors is said to improve the immune system and increase levels of the feel-good hormone dopamine in the brain.

Britain, of course, is the perfect place to try a wild swim. There are over 40,000 lakes in Britain and it's often said that wherever you are in the UK, you are always within seventy miles of a beach. If you're tempted by the idea of an open-air paddle, remember that alongside the many joys of wild swimming come significant risks. Outdoor swimming is best suited to confident, experienced swimmers and it is advisable to swim with at least one other person in case difficulties arise. Stay close to shore and do not begin by swimming in cold weather. It always pays off to plan your swim – be sure to check the water temperature, possible entry and exit points, currents and tides (where relevant), local weather conditions and the quality of the water.

Further safety advice and information can be found on the Wild Swimming website (wildswimming.co.uk) or via the Outdoor Swimmer website (outdoorswimmer.com).

LIDO REVIVAL

f you're not sold on swimming in open waters, then why not try the middle ground? An outdoor ido sits somewhere between the cosseted chlorinated climate of an indoor pool and the waves on Britain's beaches. There's little better than heading to your nearest outdoor pool on a baking summer's day and enjoying the refreshing embrace of the cool waters.

Lidos are once again making a splash around the UK as councils recognise anew the advantages of communal spaces to exercise. The 1920s and 1930s were something of a golden age for lidos in Britain. The popularity of swimming at the time led many local councils to invest in building outdoor swimming pools for the communities they served. In the lido's heyday, the UK was home to over 160 open-air pools.

Many have sadly since been closed or fully dismantled, but of those that remain, some that had fallen into disuse and disrepair are now being reopened and refurbished as the benefits of swimming are recognised. London is home to many classic examples, such as Tooting Bec Lido and Parliament Hill Lido.

If you're holidaying in or local to Devon or Cornwall, Plymouth's Tinside Lido – fed with saltwater from the nearby sea – and Penzance's Jubilee Pool in all its art deco glory are well worth stopping by for a dip. Further north, Ilkley Lido is a popular outdoor swimming spot while Nantwich Outdoor Brine Pool is the only inland brine pool left in Britain, fed by a salt spring known for its health benefits. During the Second World War, injured soldiers were even brought there to recover. Today the pool is heated to a toasty 22°C, perfect for those who prefer a cosier swim! And the best thing? Many lidos have accompanying cafés – ideal for a post-swim boost of energy.

So if you like the sound of improving your physical health while reaping the relaxing rewards of a swim, what are you waiting for? Towel, cossie and goggles at the ready!

5 INTERESTING INDOOR POOLS

London Aquatics Centre, Stratford
If you have Olympian ambitions, there's no better place to swim than the site of the 2012 Summer Olympics swimming events. And even if your goals are less lofty, the three-pool venue makes for an inspiring dip, with an undulating roof designed to mimic waves.

Mounts Baths, Northampton
Original art deco baths are often of the open-air variety, but Mounts Baths – built on the site of a former prison – has been offering architectural goodness since 1931. The sweeping pillars and tiled saunas ensure an atmospheric swim.

Cardiff International Pool, Cardiff
This Olympic-sized pool in the Welsh capital has something for all the family – enough space for adults to get a good workout in, and a separate area for childlike fun, complete with slides and rapids.

Newcastle City Baths, Newcastle
Built in a new Georgian style, these municipal Turkish baths opened in 1928 and feature two pools. Following a community-led restoration project, the baths reopened in 2020 for swimming and sauna fans to enjoy. The facility is next door to the city's concert hall, so observant swimmers may catch a few notes of the opera while doing their laps!

Moseley Road Baths, Birmingham
This community pool is the oldest Grade II-listed swimming facility in the country, having first opened its doors to keen swimmers back in 1907. Try out your backstroke to get the best views of the building's grand Gothic features.

WEBSITES
swimming.org
britishswimming.org
wildswimming.co.uk
outdoorswimmer.com
better.org.uk

If you go down to the woods today...

Forests are an essential part of the world's ecosystem, covering a third of our planet, and they are amazing places to spend time. Beautiful and calming, the world would be a very different place without them – and so would we.

ı fact, the world as we know it would not exist t all without forests. We depend on the woods or our survival – they provide the air we breathe, ne wood we use to build houses, and the paper ve write on, not to mention countless habitats or a diverse assortment of living creatures eyond the human.

And that's not all, of course: forests also have nany environmental benefits that cannot be verestimated. The world's woods help to cushion hanges to the climate, reduce soil erosion and emove carbon from the atmosphere. And of ourse, the views can be pretty breathtaking.

In today's fast-paced and high-tech world, fe can feel like it is moving at a breakneck ace. Spending time in forests can provide a velcome relief from this feeling – offering many hances to slow down, rest and recharge. And f you're based in the UK, you're really spoiled or choice. These verdant isles are home to .2 million hectares of woodland and these areas re incredibly diverse, ranging from temperate ainforests (yes, really!) to native conifer woods nd smaller urban woodlands.

It is only relatively recently that our connection o the woods and the wilderness has waned. Most of our evolution as humans took place deep in nature. Our ancestors relied on their natural surroundings for food and building materials. It is really only in the last two centuries, following the Industrial Revolution, that our interactions with the outdoors have dramatically decreased. Returning to nature gives us a chance to subconsciously remember the way we used to live more at one with the land and the seasons. This can bring us into a state of heightened sensory awareness – a feeling of being calm and yet observant. Some describe it as a feeling of returning home, bringing a deep sense of peace.

The Japanese have been clued up on the benefits of time spent in the forest for many years. There, the practice of shinrin-yoku – which translates as 'forest bathing' – was introduced by the government in the 1980s as a way to alleviate stress among harried businessmen. Forest bathing sees participants spending uninterrupted chunks of time deep in the forest, breathing deeply and opening their senses to their surroundings. Each year around 5 million Japanese citizens are estimated to participate, relieving stress and revitalising their bodies and minds among the trees and birdsong.

The advantages of this type of activity are many. Forest bathing inhibits the production of stress hormones, lowers blood pressure and subdues the 'fight or flight' reaction that kicks in when we feel stressed or anxious. Many of the original participants of Japan's forest bathing scheme reported being happier and calmer, enjoying better sleep and feeling more at home in their bodies.

Part of the reason why being in the depths of a forest is wonderful is because it is such an all-encompassing sensory experience. Nature is never silent. Spend an hour in the woods and you'll likely hear wind rushing through the trees, the crunch of leaves underfoot, the splutter of streams passing down valleys and birds calling out to one another. And yet the sounds of the outside world are dulled, as the trees cast a hush over traffic sounds and other noise pollution.

Even if you don't happen to live near a forest, these benefits can still be enjoyed. Several smartphone apps allow you to play forest sounds as background noise and many people swear by them to help them drift off to sleep. The science backs that up, too: just as a walk in the woods can calm your heart rate, so too can a nature recording. Search 'nature sounds' or similar on a mobile app store to find an array of options, many of them free to download. Forestry Englan also has an online 360° forest bathing video and gallery. Studies have shown that even looking at treescapes through a screen can relax the body.

The benefits of trees can also be appreciated from a distance. A 1984 medical study* found that patients recovering from an operation in rooms that looked out onto green space made progress more quickly and experienced lower levels of depression than those whose windows faced other buildings.

Connecting with forests has many benefits, bu always comes back to the idea of an invitation. An invitation to shift our perspective, reconnect with ourselves and appreciate the bigger picture of how we are connected to nature. Woods are vital to the ecosystems that give us life. And yet they give us much beyond that too. The invitatio to go down to the woods today is always there; we just have to be open to accepting it.

INTERNATIONAL DAY OF FORESTS: 21 MARCH

The UN General Assembly declared 21 March the International Day of Forests in 2012 to celebrate and promote awareness of the importance of all types of forests. Nations are encouraged to host local, national and international efforts that raise awareness of the significance of forests and trees, for example by organising tree planting events.

FANTASTIC FORESTS AROUND THE UK

rizedale, Cumbria

rizedale sits at the heart of the Lake District /orld Heritage Site and offers the sort of reathtaking views you'd expect from an area f such world-renowned beauty. It can be asily explored on foot, mountain bike or even orseback. Keep your eyes peeled for the unusual culptures dotted throughout the forest.

alloway Forest Park, Dumfries & Galloway

cotland's Galloway Forest is often nicknamed the ighlands of the lowlands' thanks to its stunning eauty, ancient woodland habitats and fantastic /alking opportunities. It's also a certified dark kies park, so it's an ideal spot for stargazing.

shdown Forest, East Sussex

his vast area of public space is found in the High Veald Area of Outstanding Natural Beauty, so orgeous scenery is guaranteed. The woodland is robably better known, however, as the location f the Hundred Acre Wood made famous by A.A. Ailne's Winnie the Pooh stories.

Sherwood Forest, Nottingham

Could this be the UK's most famous forest? Perhaps, given its connections with the well-known legend of Robin Hood. It is also home to the Major Oak, a tree thought to be around 1000 years old and the very spot where Robin Hood and his Merry Men are said to have spent the night.

Tollymore National Forest Park, Northern Ireland

This was the first state forest park in Northern Ireland and has the claim to fame of providing the oak wood used to furnish the cabins on the Titanic. The forest is full of curiosities, from bridges to grottoes to giant redwoods, as well as striking trees like monkey puzzle and eucalyptus.

HOW TO FOREST BATHE

ook

orest medicine works best /hen you stroll or dawdle, ather than embarking on a risk hike. Unlike walking in owns and cities, being among rees invites us to soften our aze. Natural beauty is soothing nd relaxes the mind as a result.

isten

witch off any devices so you von't be interrupted by the uzz of notifications. Then ind a comfortable spot to sit r stand, close your eyes and ust listen. What can you hear? Count how many different ounds you can hear. Open your yes. What can you hear but ot see? Can you hear the deep ilence that forms the backdrop to the sounds of the forest? If you're out with another person, agree to be silent so you can really listen.

Breathe

Take long breaths deep into the abdomen. Extending the exhalation of air to twice the length of the inhalation sends a message to the body that it can relax. Let your breath expand through your body, breathing beyond the abdomen into your fingers and toes.

Smell

As you breathe in, note what you can smell. The piney smell of conifers? The fresh scent of the forest air? Focusing on smell instead of sight, for example, can completely change your perspective and allow you to notice subtle scents.

Touch

Your connection with nature is deepened by touch. Collect some fallen leaves and feel their crisp crunch between your fingers. On a warm day, you could even take off your shoes and feel the mossy earth beneath your feet. Rub the bark of a tree, or gently brush your hands along foliage as you pass.

WEBSITES

woodlandtrust.org.uk
forestryengland.uk
countryfile.com
visitengland.com

*Study by Roger Ulrich.

The pleasure of a potager

A kitchen garden needn't be merely productive. Beauty and bounty can co-exist in an ornamental vegetable plot or container, in the form of eye-catching flowers, edibles and herbs that combine a mixture of colour, texture and form. In fact, the French have been mastering it for centuries...

When you think of vegetable growing, you might initially picture precise rows of one type of plant, bare soil between them. A potager garden, by contrast, represents the very opposite of this. Beauty is elevated and every square inch of soil is utilised for both productive and picturesque means. A fundamental characteristic of a kitchen potager is its beds where fruits, vegetables, edible flowers and fragrant herbs intermingle. Plants are carefully chosen to produce fresh food and cut flowers for as long as possible throughout the growing season. And for their aesthetic properties. Food and flowers needn't be at odds with one another, in fact they can happily coexist.

PRACTICAL & PRODUCTIVE

A potager garden is by definition an ornamental kitchen garden – designed to be both practical and productive as well as beautiful to look upon. The practice is thought to have first been brought to life by monks in medieval France. This is why traditional potagers were (and often still are) designed in the shape of a cross, a nod to the potager's religious origins.

The term 'potage' translates literally as a 'thick and hearty soup' and the name was given to this style of kitchen garden because, in ideal conditions, all of the ingredients for this soup could be grown in a potager kitchen garden!

GRAND DESIGNS

While the potager has humble monastic roots, the idea was embellished upon during France's 16th century renaissance, and potagers of the period were often seen as a feature of ornate palace gardens featuring cascading fountains, statues and a grand architectural backdrop. One of the most famous, large-scale potagers is the Potager du Roi Versailles near the Palace of Versailles. It was created in the late 17th century and produced fruits, vegetables and flowers for the court of Louis XIV of France. It has now been cultivated for over 300 years and is open to visitors, who can marvel at the 450 varieties of fruit trees and over 300 varieties of fruit and vegetables on show. At its prime, its upkeep required round-the-clock work by 30 gardeners on the garden that sprawled over 25 acres.

GROW YOUR OWN POTAGER

Most of us home gardeners won't have ambitions on such a grand scale, or the space to realise them even if we did! However, creating a beautiful, bountiful potager of your own is very much within the means of most small-scale gardeners, regardless of how much room you have to work with. Potagers are designed to be low-maintenance, too.

TIPS FOR PLANNING YOUR POTAGER

- Sketch out a rough design on paper before you break ground, including any walkways or pathways, and the shape of the beds.
- Often potagers incorporate a central focal point in the middle of the bed – think of a wigwam overflowing with sweet peas or climbing beans, or an archway covered in trailing plants. Of course, you can design your garden to your liking, but having a central area that draws the eye in is popular for a reason.
- Focus on colour, texture and contrast for maximum visual interest. Clean edges and pathways will also help to unify the space.
- Plant snugly, rather than in straight rows. Tight planting layouts ensure you get the most out of your space and are also pleasing to the eye, creating an appearance of abundance!
- The plants traditionally grown as part of potagers thrive best in full sun, so bear this in mind when choosing where to plant. The advantage of containers is that they can be moved around depending on the plant's needs and available daylight. On a shady plot, choose herbs (e.g. mint) and flowers that will tolerate lower light levels.
- You may choose to use edible plants like lavender, rosemary or marjoram as edging plants – and the bees will thank you too!
- Make a list of the herbs you like to cook with and be sure to incorporate these into your potager garden.
- Perennials like rhubarb, asparagus, fruit trees, globe artichokes and nine-star broccoli provide almost year-round interest, if you are lucky enough to have the space.
- Edible flowers will make your potager even more productive: try nigella, nasturtium and borage for starters, and see the recipe on p117.
- Blooms that attract hungry pollinators will ensure a thriving potager - think calendula, echinacea, sunflowers and cornflowers.

A modern-day potager in the spirit of the original should be based on the following aims: supplying the garden with a steady supply of fresh, edible, delicious produce. It should maintain interest most of the year as well as provide cut flowers and herbs. When planning a potager container garden, colour, flavour, fragrance and beauty are all important factors.

Colour is a very important part of designing an ornamental kitchen garden like a potager. This might mean selecting seed varieties with their shade in mind: there are interestingly coloured versions of many popular vegetables, such as purple carrots, red Brussels sprouts and yellow courgettes. Plumping for contrasting colours can be really pleasing to the eye: pairing bright orange nasturtium flowers with leafy greens, for example, or vivid blue cornflowers with the equally eye-catching red of tomato fruits.

Keep your eye out for two-toned varieties, which also add visual interest. Variegated thyme, sage and oregano are widely available.

THE SHAPE OF THINGS

Just as significant to consider are structure and form. Hard structures will provide interest in the winter months when green shoots are thin on the ground, at least in the UK. Think arches, obelisks, wigwams and hard-landscaped edging. These needn't be expensive or even designed for that purpose. Using branches or hazel sticks to make your own plant supports is easy and pretty much free if you have your own trees or the time to go out hunting for them.

Height can also come in the form of plants themselves. Artichokes and sunflowers can tower above humans, growing to heights over 6 feet, and of course provide edible joy in the form of their fruit and seeds and petals. Climbing plants come in particularly handy here, too. Trailing squash or climbing beans work especially well in ornamental kitchen gardens, and it's worth seeking out notably beautiful varieties to make your potager as aesthetically pleasing as possible.

For climbing beans, try borlotti beans or

ɿeirloom varieties of runner beans, which often ɿave white flowers instead of the usual red. ;quash varieties well-suited to the task include .romboncino squash, which produces mountains ɔf curly green fruit, or trailing yellow courgettes, vhich add interesting colour.

ᴘERFECT PAIRINGS

ᴇssential to the idea of a productive potager is :he concept of companion planting. That's the ɔrganic practice of combining plants and flowers :hat work well together, in the hope of improving ɔollination and reducing pest damage.

Particularly pretty protective pairings include :alendula and tomatoes, and nasturtiums ɹnderplanted around vulnerable vegetable ɔlants like kale, broccoli and beans. The smell of calendula is said to deter hungry pests, while the nasturtiums will attract aphids and the like instead, leaving your precious vegetables to grow on in peace.

And a potager garden won't just make you and any human visitors to your garden happy. It'll also please insects and animals passing through, offering a safe haven for many essential pollinators and invertebrates. As green space dwindles, creating varied and wildlife-friendly gardens is more important than ever.

Growing a gorgeous potager is also great fun and quick to achieve over a spring and summer, especially if you choose fast-growing annuals. And best of all, a feast for the senses also becomes a feast for you to tuck into come harvest time. So let's hear it for the humble potager.

HOW TO: POTAGER IN A POT

Although many of France's most beautiful and historic potager gardens exist on a large scale, it's just as easy (and undoubtedly much more achievable!) to create your own potager at home in a container. Whether you have a raised bed, a large pot or only a window box, the potager style of gardening can be recreated in a space of almost any size. The basics are easy to remember: combine productive edible plants with flowers, add height for interest and consider the seasons by picking plants that bloom at different times of year. If possible, choose plants that bloom over a long period rather than those that bloom briefly for only a short season. For a happy potager window box, combine chives, calendula or marigolds, marjoram and lemon thyme with trailing nasturtiums planted along the front edge that will overhang the window ledge for structural interest. To keep it looking its best for longer, pick the herbs regularly and deadhead the flowers once they've gone over to encourage a flush of new growth.

WEBSITES

rhs.org.uk
chateauvillandry.fr
wmf.org/project/potager-du-roi

Rich pickings

In streets, fields, woodland and meadows, food exists waiting to be picked. And not just any food: from plump blackberries to pungent wild garlic, crunchy hazelnuts and fragrant elderflowers, the delicious delights that line our fields and hedgerows are often hiding in plain sight.

Foraging is, put simply, the act of gathering wild food. Although it's gained greater popularity in recent years, foraging would have been a way of life for our distant ancestors. Our hunter-gatherer predecessors sustained themselves by hunting animals and picking wild fruits and vegetables from their immediate surroundings, until the invention of modern farming 10,000 years ago.

And foraging has often seen spikes in acceptance in times of hardship and need. As recently as the Second World War, for example. Importing oranges was banned due to wartime import restrictions, so foraged rosehips provided a source of vitamin C for hungry Britons and were often made into a syrup that claimed to banish coughs and colds.

Today foraging is back in fashion, driven by frugality and a shift towards sustainable diets.

And it's not just the preserve of rural lanes – seeking out wild food is often as achievable in large cities. Parks, riversides and small woodlands are often treasure troves of forage-able food.

As daffodils emerge from bare soil and birds return song to the skies, many edible wild plants are just getting going too. For some, the powerful scent of wild garlic is a sure sign spring has arrived. The leafy edible likes damp soil, so you'll often find it carpeting river banks. Young leaves emerge by March or April. Snip leaves at the base, leaving the bulb intact. Use your bounty in stir fries, mixed into mash or in a wild garlic pesto.

By late May a different scent fills the air, both in city parks and country lanes – that of aromatic elderflower, blossom of the elder tree. The starry clusters of cream flowers can be picked in May and June. Elderflower cordial is the most well-known use for these fragrant flowers, but you can also make jellies, sorbets, flavoured gins and teas (p45).

In summer, plants more often decried as weeds can also be enjoyed in meals. While dandelions and nettles probably aren't top of your teatime menu, both have their uses. Instead of chucking them on the compost, try brewing up nettle tea or blending a nettle pesto. Dandelion greens can be added to salads, while the flowers make an alternative to honey when cooked with sugar (p45).

By late summer and autumn, foragers will find rich pickings around the UK. Hedgerows are thick with luscious bounty, from apples and blackberries to the less routine mulberries, rosehips and hazelnuts. The latter ripen in September and October and are ready to eat once the papery coating starts to pull away from the nut. You can also pick hazelnuts 'in the green' and ripen in a paper bag somewhere cool and dark. Once ripe, remove the hard outer shell before eating as is or whizz into veggie burgers (p44).

As the chill sets in, branches become bare and there's less to forage. But early winter is the best time to pick sloe berries. Sloes are the fruit of the blackthorn bush, a spiny shrub that belongs to the rose family, and found across the UK in great numbers. The inky berries are traditionally used to make sloe gin, a sweet and aromatic liqueur. If you're picking the berries to make this gin, it's customary to wait until after the first frost when the fruits are sweeter. You can also use sloes to add a plummy flavour to jellies and syrups.

Beginners are likely to find success with quick wins that are easy to identify and straightforward to prepare, like blackberries (p44). And often the thrill of the chase is as fun as the treasure, offering an excuse to discover your local area and perhaps find something utterly delicious for nothing.

FORAGING ADVICE FOR BEGINNERS

- When foraging on public walkways, always try to pick items that are set back slightly from the main drag to avoid contamination by car fumes and animal activity.
- Pick sparingly: the golden rule of picking wild food is to leave some behind, whether for other keen foragers, wildlife or to preserve the plant so it will continue to flourish and nourish year after year.
- When picking in hedgerows, especially if on the hunt for sloes or blackberries, it's advisable to wear gloves to avoid prickly branches. And of course, especially thick protection is needed to pick stinging nettles.
- Err on the side of caution. If you're not totally sure what you're picking, it is wise to leave it behind. Plants that have the potential to be poisonous, such as mushrooms, should be left to the professionals.
- Make sure you are not hunting for food on private property. Stick to areas you know have public right of way.
- Several organisations now run foraging courses for those wanting to deepen their knowledge. Check out Wild Food UK and Totally Wild, as well as seeking out options in your local area.

WEBSITES

wildfooduk.com
totallywilduk.co.uk
woodlandtrust.org.uk
eatweeds.co.uk

Serves 4 • Time 50 mins
Calories 360
Fibre 5.6g • Salt 0.2g • Sugar 29g
Fat 12.2g of which 7g is saturated

ORCHARD SPONGE PUDDING  

Plums 250g (9oz), stoned and thickly sliced
Cooking apples 450g (1lb), cored, peeled and sliced
Blackberries 150g (5oz)
Caster sugar 110g (4oz)
Small orange 1, grated zest and juice
Butter 50g (2oz)
Self-raising flour 75g (3oz)
Egg 1
Sifted icing sugar to decorate (optional)
Custard to serve (optional)

1 Preheat oven to 180°C/160°fan/Gas 4. Put plums, apples and blackberries into a 1.25 litre (2 pint) ovenproof pie dish. Sprinkle over half sugar and half orange juice then bake for 10 minutes.
2 Put remaining sugar with orange zest, butter, flour and egg into a bowl and beat together until smooth. Gradually beat in remaining orange juice, being careful not to over-mix or the topping may split.
3 Flatten partially cooked fruit slightly with the back of a spoon, then spoon sponge mixture over the top and spread into an even layer. Bake for 25-30 minutes until topping is well risen and golden and springs back when pressed with a fingertip. Dust with icing sugar and serve warm with custard, if using.

Serves 4 • Time 25 mins plus chilling
Calories 395
Fibre 10.3g • Salt 0.8g • Sugar 0g
Fat 27.5g of which 2.8g is saturated

HAZELNUT VEGGIE BURGERS  

Olive oil 5 tbsp
Onion 1, peeled and finely chopped
Celery 1 stick, trimmed and finely chopped
Carrot 1, peeled and grated
Whole blanched hazelnuts 100g packet
Mixed pulses 420g tin, drained
Fresh chopped parsley 3 tbsp
Wholemeal flour 2 tbsp
Buns and salad to serve (optional)

1 Heat 1 tbsp oil in a frying pan and gently fry vegetables, stirring, for 5 minutes until softened. Set aside.
2 Meanwhile, finely grind half the hazelnuts in a blender and chop remainder. Heat a frying pan until very hot then add ground and chopped nuts. Cook, stirring constantly, for about 2 minutes, until nuts turn light brown. Allow to cool.
3 Mash pulses to a thick paste, then stir in cooked vegetables, nuts, parsley and season with salt and freshly ground black pepper. Mix well, cover and chill for 1 hour.
4 Divide mixture into 4 equal portions and form each into a 10cm (4in) burger with wet hands. Put flour on a plate and season. Lightly coat each burger on both sides with flour.
5 Heat remaining oil in a large frying pan and gently fry burgers for 10-12 minutes, turning halfway through, until lightly golden on both sides. Drain well. Serve on buns with salad, if liked.

ELDERFLOWER & STRAWBERRY ICED TEA 

Drying elderflowers could not be easier: simply hang up somewhere cool and dry. Forage in the early morning or evening when the flowers are not wilting from the midday sun.

Dried elderflowers 5 tbsp
Caster sugar 1.5kg (3lb 5oz)
Citric acid 50g (2oz)
Ripe strawberries 450g (1lb), hulled and halved
Crushed ice and sparkling water or lemonade to serve (optional)

1 Place elderflowers in a large container that has a tight-fitting lid. Add sugar and citric acid, then pour over 2.5 litres (4 pints) boiling water. Stir to mix.
2 Leave to cool slightly before adding strawberries, pressing against the sides of the container to lightly crush.
3 Cover and leave for 3 days in a cool dark place, stirring twice a day.
4 Strain tea into bottles. Seal and store in a cool place. Serve over crushed ice topped up with sparkling water or lemonade, if you like.

Makes 2.5 litres (4 pints)
Time 20 mins plus 3 days resting
Calories 114
Fibre 0.3g • Salt 0g • Sugar 29.7g
Fat 0g of which 0g is saturated

DANDELION 'HONEY' 

Despite what the name suggests, dandelion honey is not produced by bees like conventional honey. Rather, it's a sweet, honey-like syrup made from the yellow flowers and sugar. It also makes a wonderful vegan substitute for ordinary honey.

Dandelion flowers 350g (12oz), green parts removed
Lemon 1, thinly sliced
Golden granulated sugar 750g (1lb 10oz)

1 Simmer dandelion heads and sliced lemon in 1 litre (1¾ pints) water for 20 minutes in a covered pan. Pour into a glass bowl and cover. Leave to steep overnight.

2 Pour mixture through a sieve or muslin cloth, pressing down with a spoon to get about 750ml (1¼ pints) liquid. Discard flower heads.

3 Simmer liquid in a pan, uncovered, with sugar for about 45 minutes or until the mixture becomes syrupy and drips slowly off a spoon.

4 Pour syrup into 2 sterilised glass jars, seal and leave to cool. Your dandelion honey will keep, unopened and refrigerated, for up to a year.

Makes enough to fill 2 medium jam jars
Time 1 hr 20 mins plus overnight steeping
Calories 42
Fibre 0g • Salt 0g • Sugar 11.3g
Fat 0g of which 0g is saturated

DRY WEIGHT CONVERSIONS

grams (g)	ounces (oz)
15	½
25	1
50	2
75	3
110	4 (¼lb)
150	5
175	6
200	7
225	8 (½lb)
250	9
275	10
300	11
350	12 (¾lb)
375	13
400	14
425	15
450	16 (1lb)
500	1lb 2oz
680	1½lb
750	1lb 10oz
900	2lb

These quantities are not exact, but they have been calculated to give proportionately correct measurements.

SPOON MEASURES

1 tablespoon	=	3 level teaspoons
1 level tablespoon	=	15ml
1 level teaspoon	=	5ml
If greater accuracy is not required:		
1 rounded teaspoon	=	2 level teaspoons
1 heaped teaspoon	=	3 level teaspoons or 1 level tablespoon

LIQUID CONVERSIONS

millilitres (ml)	fluid ounces (fl oz)	US cups
15	½	1 tbsp (level)
30	1	⅛
60	2	¼
90	3	⅜
125	4	½
150	5 (¼ pint)	⅔
175	6	¾
225	8	1
300	10 (½ pint)	1¼
350	12	1½
450	16	2
500	18	2¼
600	20 (1 pint)	2½
900	1½ pints	3¾
1 litre	1¾ pints	1 quart (4 cups)
1.25 litres	2 pints	1¼ quarts
1.5 litres	2½ pints	3 US pints
2 litres	3½ pints	2 quarts

These quantities are not exact, but they have been calculated to give proportionately correct measurements.

CAKE TIN CONVERSIONS

Round tin	Square tin
15cm (6in)	13cm (5in)
20cm (8in)	18cm (7in)
23cm (9in)	20cm (8in)
28cm (11in)	25.5cm (10in)

A square cake tin holds 25% more than a round tin of the same size. If using a square tin when the recipe says to use a round one, turn during baking, as the edges will cook faster than the centre.

GRILLING TIMES: FISH

	minutes each side
Cod (steak)	5–6
Dover sole (fillet)	2–3
Halibut (steak)	5–6
Herring (whole)	4–5
Mackerel (whole)	6–7
Monkfish (steak)	5–6
Plaice (whole)	4–6
Plaice (fillet)	2–3
Salmon (steak)	5–6
Skate	5–6
Tuna (steak)	1–2

Times given for fish weighing approximately 175–225g (6–8oz).

OVEN TEMPERATURES

°C	(fan)	°F	gas	description
110	(90)	225	¼	cool
120/130	(100/110)	250	½	cool
140	(120)	275	1	very low
150	(130)	300	2	very low
160/170	(140/150)	325	3	low to moderate
180	(160)	350	4	moderate
190	(170)	375	5	moderately hot
200	(180)	400	6	hot
220	(200)	425	7	hot
230	(210)	450	8	hot
240	(220)	475	9	very hot

Guide to recommended equivalent settings, not exact conversions. Always refer to your cooker instruction book.

ROASTING TIMES: MEAT*

Set oven temperature to 180°C/160°fan/Gas 4.

	cooking time per 450g/1lb	extra cooking time
Beef		
rare	20 mins	20 mins
medium	25 mins	25 mins
well done	30 mins	30 mins
Lamb		
medium	25 mins	25 mins
well done	30 mins	30 mins
Pork		
medium	30 mins	30 mins
well done	35 mins	35 mins

Let the cooked meat rest for 5–15 minutes before carving to allow the juices to be reabsorbed and to make carving easier.

STEAMING TIMES: VEGETABLES

	minutes
Asparagus	5–7
Beansprouts	3–4
Beetroot (sliced)	5–7
Broccoli (florets)	5–7
Brussels sprouts	5–7
Cabbage (chopped)	4–6
Carrots (thickly sliced)	5–7
Cauliflower (florets)	5–7
Courgettes (sliced)	3–5
Green beans	5–7
Leeks	5–8
Mangetout peas	3–5
Peas	3–5
Potatoes (cubed)	5–7

Times given are for steaming from when water has started to boil.

ROASTING TIMES: POULTRY*

	oven temperature	cooking time per 450g/1lb	extra cooking time	resting time
Chicken	220°C/200°fan/Gas 7 for 20 mins; then 190°C/170°fan/Gas 5	20 mins	20 mins	15 mins
Turkey (stuffed weight)	220°C/200°fan/Gas 7 uncovered for 30 mins; then, covered, 190°C/170°fan/Gas 5; then for last 30 mins, uncovered, 200°C/180°fan/Gas 6	18 mins	18 mins	30 mins
Duck	230°C/210°fan/Gas 8 for 20 mins; then 180°C/160°fan/Gas 4	15 mins	—	15 mins

*Note that for fan ovens, cooking times are generally reduced by 10 minutes for every hour. These timings and oven temperatures are guidelines – follow instructions on packaging if possible.

How to get your 5 a day

A balanced diet contains at least five different portions of fruit and vegetables a day and a good mix throughout the week.

Sometimes eating healthily can feel like a minefield in the face of so much conflicting advice. Still, we all know eating enough fruit and veg is crucial for good health. It needn't be confusing: at its best, getting your 5 a day can be simple and delicious. Each number below represents 1 of your 5 a day.

RED

Tomato	1
Cherry tomatoes	7
Rhubarb (cooked)	2 tbsp
Strawberries	7
Cherries	14
Pepper	½

ORANGE

Orange	1
Nectarine	1
Apricots	3
Carrots	3 tbsp
Baked beans	3 tbsp
Sweet potato	1

YELLOW

Banana	1
Grapefruit	½
Pineapple	1 slice
Sweetcorn	3 tbsp
Yellow lentils	3 tbsp
Chickpeas	3 tbsp

GREEN

Apple	1
Melon	1 slice
Lettuce	1 bowl
Peas	3 tbsp
Green beans	4 tbsp
Avocado	½

PURPLE

Plums	2
Blackcurrants	4 tbsp
Sultanas	1 tbsp
Kidney beans	3 tbsp
Beetroot	7 slices
Aubergine	½

WHITE

Leek	1
Cauliflower	8 florets
Mushrooms (chopped)	3 tbsp
Turnip/swede	3 tbsp
Butter beans	3 tbsp
Parsnip	1

EAT THE RAINBOW

Try to choose each portion from a different colour group. Aiming for a colourful plate can be a simple way to get the full range of vitamins and minerals your body needs. And your meals will be beautiful, too!

WHAT COUNTS?

Almost all fruits and vegetables count towards your 5 a day. This includes fresh produce, frozen, tinned and preserved fruits and vegetables.

One portion of your 5 a day...
= 80g of fruit
= 80g of vegetables
= 30g dried fruit

DID YOU KNOW...?

Mixing fruits or vegetables (e.g. 40g banana and 40g strawberries) still counts towards your total as long as each portion adds up to 80g.

Fruit juices and smoothies only count as one portion, no matter how many glasses you drink. The NHS recommends no more than 150ml a day.

Pulses, beans and legumes, like lentils, kidney beans or chickpeas, only count as one portion of your 5 a day, regardless of how many 80g portions you eat.

Potatoes don't count towards your 5 a day because of their high starch content, but they are still a great source of fibre, potassium and B vitamins. However, sweet potatoes do count.

Washing instructions

TEXTILE CYCLES

Check both the temperature, given by the figure in the tub, and the machine-action, shown by the bar(s) under it. The temperature may be indicated by dots (six for 95°, four for 60°, two for 40° and one for 30°).

Maximum agitation. Cotton cycle
White cotton or linen articles without special finishes.

Maximum agitation. Cotton cycle
Cotton or linen articles without special finishes where colours are fast at 60°C.

Maximum agitation. Cotton cycle
Cotton or linen where colours are fast at 40°C but not at 60°C.

Medium agitation. Synthetic cycle
Acrylics, acetate or triacetate, including mixtures with wool, polyester and wool blends.

Minimum agitation. Wool cycle
Wool, including blankets, wool mixed with other fibres, viscose and silk.

Gentle agitation. Delicates cycle
Silk, acetates and mixed synthetics not colourfast at 40°C.

Hand wash only
See garment label for further instructions.

Do not machine or hand wash

DRY-CLEANING

The letter P or F indicates the cleaning fluids that may be used by your professional dry-cleaner.

May be dry-cleaned

Do not dry-clean

BLEACHING

Bleach may be used

Do not bleach

Do not use chlorine bleach

DRYING SYMBOLS

Check the label to see if your garment can be tumble-dried. The label may advise using a reduced heat setting by putting a single dot within the circle. Two dots indicate a higher heat setting.

May be tumble-dried

Drip dry recommended

Do not tumble-dry

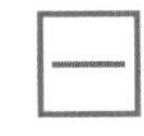

Dry flat

Hang dry

IRONING

- The dots inside the iron indicate the temperature setting. One dot represents the coolest setting and three dots are for the hottest temperature. The table (right) is a guide to the temperature to use for specific types of fabric.
- You should always use the setting recommended by the manufacturer. For some materials the advice may be that you iron on the wrong side of the fabric only, so check the label.
- To avoid creases, store your clothes in drawers and wardrobes loosely; don't pack them in.

Hot (3 dots)
Cotton and linen fabrics.

Warm (2 dots)
Polyester mixtures and wool.

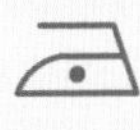

Cool (1 dot)
Acrylic, nylon, acetate, triacetate, viscose and polyester.

Do not iron

ECO LAUNDRY

To limit the environmental impact of laundry, wash garments sparingly. Launder only if they look or smell dirty and try to wash at 30°C.

Stain removal

The most important factor in attacking stains is to act swiftly. The newer the stain, whether greasy, non-greasy, or a combination of the two, the easier it will be to remove without damage.

First and foremost, check what processes and cleaning agents are suitable for the stained item. Wool and silk often need to be treated differently from cotton and synthetics, for example. Always check care labels if possible, and follow what they say.

Likewise, bear in mind that whites may need to be treated differently from coloureds. In any case, always check for colourfastness before soaking.

Biological detergent works well even at low temperatures due to the enzymes it contains. Whenever you can, use it for stain removal but don't use it, or any other enzyme-based cleaner, on wool or silk. For hand-washing, old or delicate fabrics and baby clothes, use a mild non-biological detergent.

Some of the cleaning agents you will need contain chemicals that are poisonous or flammable. Always read the packaging carefully and store them away from children.

For your safety, work in an area that has plenty of ventilation.

CLEANING KIT

Bicarbonate of soda: Use this – or cornflour or talcum powder – to absorb grease and oil.

Borax: Boosts your detergent's performance.

Detergents: Biological/non-biological/heavy-duty/mild. Liquid detergent is good for oily stains and as a pre-wash treatment.

Eucalyptus oil: Available from major chemists. Good for treating greasy stains.

Glycerine: For treating old stains before washing.

Hydrogen peroxide: Ask your chemist for 3%, which is 10 volume strength (VS). Don't use on wool or silk.

Methylated spirits: From DIY stores. Apply with cotton buds. Don't use on fabric that contains acetate or triacetate.

Pre-wash treatments: Some are for common stains, some are more specific. Follow the manufacturer's instructions.

White distilled vinegar: Use as a solution of 15ml vinegar to 300ml water (3tsp to ½ pint); or mixed to a paste with bicarbonate of soda.

White spirit: Available from DIY stores. Good for treating paint and grease stains.

WHAT TO DO

- Remove any solids with a blunt knife, and blot liquids with white kitchen paper.
- Apply stain remover to a small, unseen area and wait 5–10 minutes. If the fabric reacts, or if in doubt, seek dry-cleaning advice. Avoid treating delicate or expensive fabrics, or those that require dry-cleaning only.
- Don't over-soak the fabric with a cleaning agent. To avoid making a ring mark, use a soft, absorbent cloth to apply the cleaning agent and work in a circular motion from the outside inwards. Dab, rather than rub, because rubbing can damage the fabric and it can also spread the stain.

PERSONAL

Blood: Soak in cold water with biological detergent or salt; or rub in a paste of bicarb and cold water, leave to dry, brush off. Wash in biological detergent (if appropriate for the fabric).
Make-up: Work in biological liquid detergent; wash as usual.
Perspiration: Sponge with white vinegar, rinse and soak in salt solution or biological detergent. Soften old stains with glycerine. Rinse, wash as usual.
Urine: Rinse in cold water; dab with hydrogen peroxide, or soak in biological detergent; rinse, wash as usual. For pet urine, soak in soda water, blot excess, sponge with salty water, rinse and blot dry. Sprinkle with bicarb, leave for a while, then vacuum.
Vomit: Rinse under running cold water; soak in a sterilising solution, or biological detergent with some disinfectant added; wash as usual.

FOOD AND DRINKS

Chocolate: Rinse in cold water; apply biological detergent and soak overnight if necessary; wash in suitable detergent.
Coffee: Soak in lukewarm water, use a pre-wash treatment and wash in suitable detergent.
Egg: Dab with cold salty water; wash in biological detergent.
Gravy: Soak in cold water with biological detergent; usual wash.
Grease: Cover with bicarb, leave for an hour; brush off. Soak in liquid detergent and wash in water as hot as the fabric allows.
Milk and fruit juice: Rinse under running cold water, then soak in biological detergent and wash in water as hot as the fabric allows.
Oil/salad dressings: Blot and dab with biological liquid detergent; or sprinkle with bicarb, brush off and soak in washing-up liquid. Usual wash.
Tea: Treat as coffee but wash in heavy-duty detergent; or dab with lemon juice, rinse and wash in biological detergent; or pour white vinegar solution, leave for 10 mins and wash.
Tomato sauce: Dab gently with biological liquid detergent and wash as usual; or rinse in cold water, dab with white vinegar, rinse and wash as usual.
Wine, red: Pour soda water over the stain, blot, cover with salt and leave for 30 minutes. Soak in cold water; sponge with biological detergent and wash as usual. On upholstery and carpets, cover with salt, leave to absorb and brush off. Dab with warm water and biological detergent; then with cold water.
Wine, white: Rinse in warm water; dab with biological liquid detergent (white vinegar for silk and wool). Rinse and wash as usual. On upholstery and carpets, blot then sponge gently with soapy water (do not rub).

MISCELLANEOUS

Grass: Dab with methylated spirits; rinse with warm soapy water. Use an appropriate pre-wash treatment and then wash in heavy-duty detergent.
Ink (ballpoint or felt tip): Dab with diluted methylated spirits; rinse and sponge with biological detergent; wash as usual. If persistent, treat as rust.
Rust: Dab with lemon juice, cover with salt, leave for at least an hour; rinse; usual wash.
Suntan lotion: Use a pre-wash for greasy stains, or treat with eucalyptus oil or a product for removing hard-water stains. Wash in biological detergent.
Tar: Dab with eucalyptus oil on reverse of fabric; wash in biological detergent in water as hot as fabric allows.

Metric conversions

			To convert	multiply by
Length				
1 millimetre (mm)		= 0.0394in	mm to in	0.0394
1 centimetre (cm)	= 10mm	= 0.394in	cm to in	0.394
1 metre (m)	= 100cm	= 1.09yd	m to yd	1.09
1 kilometre (km)	= 1000m	= 0.621 mile	km to mi	0.621
1 inch (in)		= 2.54cm	in to cm	2.54
1 foot (ft)	= 12in	= 30.5cm	ft to cm	30.5
1 yard (yd)	= 3ft	= 0.914m	yd to m	0.914
1 mile (mi)	= 1760yd	= 1.61km	mi to km	1.61
Area				
1 sq millimetre (mm)		= 0.00155sq in	mm^2 to in^2	0.00155
1 sq centimetre (cm)	= 100sq mm	= 0.155sq in	cm^2 to in^2	0.155
1 sq metre (m)	= 10,000sq cm	= 1.2sq yd	m^2 to yd^2	1.2
1 hectare (ha)	= 10,000sq m	= 2.47a	ha to a	2.47
1 sq kilometre (km)	= 100ha	= 0.386sq mile	km^2 to mi^2	0.386
1 sq inch (in)		= 6.45sq cm	in^2 to cm^2	6.45
1 sq foot (ft)	= 144sq in	= 0.0929sq m	ft^2 to m^2	0.0929
1 sq yard (yd)	= 9sq ft	= 0.836sq m	yd^2 to m^2	0.836
1 acre (a)	= 4840sq yd	= 4047sq m	a to m^2	4047
1 sq mile (mi)	= 640a	= 2.59sq km	mi^2 to km^2	2.59
Volume				
1 cu centimetre (cm)	= 1000cu mm	= 0.0611cu in	cm^3 to in^3	0.0611
1 cu decimetre (dm)	= 1000cu cm	= 0.0353cu ft	dm^3 to ft^3	0.0353
1 cu metre (m)	= 1000cu dm	= 1.31cu yd	m^3 to yd^3	1.31
1 cu inch (in)		= 16.4cu cm	in^3 to cm^3	16.4
1 cu foot (ft)	= 1730cu in	= 28.4cu dm	ft^3 to dm^3	28.4
1 cu yard (yd)	= 27cu ft	= 0.765cu m	yd^3 to m^3	0.765
Capacity				
1 millilitre (ml)		= 0.0352fl oz	ml to fl oz	0.0352
1 centilitre (cl)	= 10ml	= 0.352fl oz	cl to fl oz	0.352
1 litre (l)	= 100cl	= 1.76pt	l to pt	1.76
1 fluid ounce (fl oz)		= 28.4ml	fl oz to ml	28.4
1 gill (gi)	= 5fl oz	= 14.2cl	gi to cl	14.2
1 pint (pt)	= 20fl oz	= 0.568l	pt to l	0.568
1 quart (qt)	= 2pt	= 1.14l	qt to l	1.14
1 gallon (gal)	= 4qt	= 4.55l	gal to l	4.55
Weight				
1 gram (g)	= 1000mg	= 0.0353oz	g to oz	0.0353
1 kilogram (kg)	= 1000g	= 2.2lb	kg to lb	2.2
1 tonne (t)	= 1000kg	= 0.984 ton	tonne to ton	0.984
1 ounce (oz)	= 438 grains	= 28.3g	oz to g	28.3
1 pound (lb)	= 16oz	= 0.454kg	lb to kg	0.454
1 stone (st)	= 14lb	= 6.35kg	st to kg	6.35
1 ton (t)	= 160st	= 1.02 tonne	ton to tonne	1.02

2023

26 Monday
Bank Holiday, UK

27 Tuesday
Bank Holiday, UK

28 Wednesday

29 Thursday

30 Friday
☽ First quarter

REMINDERS

Saturday 31
New Year's Eve

JANUARY 2023 Sunday 1
New Year's Day

BRUSSELS SPROUT SLAW

Brussels sprouts 100g (3½oz), stalks trimmed
Red or white cabbage 150g (5oz), trimmed
Carrot 1 large, peeled and grated
Baby leek 1, trimmed and thinly sliced
Reduced-fat mayonnaise 4 tbsp
Blue cheese such as Stilton 50g (2oz), crumbled
Smoked streaky bacon 4 rashers
Eating apple 1, cored and finely chopped

1 Cut sprouts and cabbage into shreds, then cut cabbage into short lengths. Mix well with carrot and leek. Cover and chill until serving.
2 Mix mayonnaise and cheese together. Cover and chill until ready to serve.
3 Just before serving, heat a dry frying pan until hot and dry-fry bacon rashers for 2 minutes on each side until crispy and cooked through. Drain well and chop.
4 Mix apple into vegetables along with blue cheese dressing and pile into a serving bowl. Sprinkle with bacon and serve as part of a salad meal or alongside cold cuts and thick chips or baked potatoes.
TIPS Leek gives a mild onion-like flavour, but for more bite, use 2 spring onions. For vegetarians, replace the bacon with fried breadcrumbs or toasted nuts or seeds.

Serves 4 • **Time 20 mins**
Calories 182 • Fibre 3.9g • Salt 0.9g • Sugar 0g
Fat 13.3g of which 4.8g is saturated

2 Monday
Bank Holiday, UK

3 Tuesday
Bank Holiday, Scotland

4 Wednesday

5 Thursday

6 Friday
Epiphany

○ Full moon

REMINDERS

Saturday 7

Sunday 8

GRIDDLED PINEAPPLE WITH SALTED CARAMEL DIP

Pineapple 1 medium, topped and tailed and skin sliced off
White chocolate chips 75g (3oz)
Salted caramel sauce 75g (3oz)
Double cream 4 tbsp
Sunflower oil 1 tsp

1 Cut pineapple in half lengthways then cut each half into six thick slices. Remove core if it is tough.
2 Put chocolate chips, caramel sauce and cream in a small pan and heat very gently, stirring, until chocolate has melted. Cover and keep warm over a low heat.
3 Heat a nonstick griddle pan until hot. Brush with a little oil and arrange half of pineapple slices on the griddle. Cook for 2-3 minutes on each side until lightly caramelised. Remove and keep warm while you cook the other batch.
4 Drain pineapple and pile onto a warmed serving plate. Pour caramel dip into small dishes and serve as a dipping sauce.

Serves 4 • Time 20 mins
Calories 383 • Fibre 2.6g • Salt 0.3g • Sugar 22.9g
Fat 23.9g of which 14.2g is saturated

9 Monday

10 Tuesday

11 Wednesday

12 Thursday

13 Friday

REMINDERS

Saturday 14

Sunday 15

(Last quarter

SWEDISH MEATBALL GRATIN

Pork mince 500g (1lb 2oz)
Echalion shallots 2, peeled and finely chopped
Garlic 1 clove, crushed
Allspice and nutmeg ¼ tsp of each
Breadcrumbs 125g (4½oz)
Egg 1, beaten
Olive oil 4 tbsp
Fennel 1 large bulb, finely sliced
Butter 50g (2oz)
Plain flour 2 tbsp
Vegetable stock 350ml (12fl oz)
Crème fraîche 100ml (3½fl oz)
Dijon mustard 2 tbsp
Soy sauce 2 tbsp
Fresh dill 25g (1oz), finely chopped, plus extra to serve
Cranberry sauce to serve (optional)

1 Combine mince, shallots, garlic, spices, 50g (2oz) breadcrumbs, egg and seasoning. Shape into 20 balls.
2 Heat 1 tbsp oil in a frying pan and fry the fennel until softened. Transfer to a 2 litre (3½ pints) ovenproof dish. Add 1 tbsp oil to the pan and fry meatballs for 3-4 minutes until golden. Transfer to the dish.
3 Melt butter in pan, stir in flour and cook for 1 minute. Whisk in stock, crème fraîche, mustard and soy; season. Simmer for 1-2 minutes to thicken. Pour over meatballs.
4 Preheat oven to 200°C/180°fan/Gas 6. Toss together dill, remaining breadcrumbs and 2 tbsp olive oil and sprinkle over the top. Bake in the oven for 25-30 minutes until golden. Garnish with extra dill and serve with cranberry sauce, if using.

Serves 4 • Time 1 hr
Calories 584 • Fibre 1.8g • Salt 2g • Sugar 0.3g
Fat 36.3g of which 13.1g is saturated

16 Monday

17 Tuesday

18 Wednesday

19 Thursday

20 Friday

REMINDERS

Saturday 21

● New moon

Sunday 22

Chinese New Year

HOISIN DUCK & CUCUMBER SUB ROLLS

Ginger 2cm (¾in), sliced
Garlic 2 cloves, peeled and sliced
Vegetable stock 500ml (18fl oz)
Rice wine 4 tbsp
Soy sauce 4 tbsp
Light brown sugar 50g (2oz)
Chinese 5-spice 1 tbsp
Duck legs 2
Hoisin sauce 3 tbsp
Mini cucumbers 2, sliced lengthways
Sub rolls 2
Spring onions 2, shredded

1 In a pan, add ginger, garlic, stock, rice wine, soy, sugar and spice. Mix together then add duck. Cover and leave to marinate in the fridge for 2-3 hours or overnight.
2 Set the pan over a high heat and bring to a simmer. Leave to cook, covered, for 1½ hours, adding a little water if it dries out too much.
3 Preheat oven to 200°C/180°fan/Gas 6. Remove duck from the liquid and place on a baking tray. Brush over 1 tbsp hoisin sauce. Transfer to oven for 15-20 minutes or until sticky and golden.
4 To serve, divide cucumber between rolls. Shred the duck and divide between rolls. Top with spring onions and a drizzle of remaining hoisin sauce.

Serves 2 • Time 1 hr 45 mins plus marinating
Calories 412 • Fibre 3.1g • Salt 5g • Sugar 28.1g
Fat 7.3g of which 1.7g is saturated

23 Monday

24 Tuesday

25 Wednesday

Burns Night

26 Thursday

27 Friday

REMINDERS

Saturday 28

) First quarter

Sunday 29

MINI VEGAN HAGGIS

Vegetable oil 1 tbsp
Chestnut mushrooms 200g (7oz), washed and finely chopped
Leek 1 medium, trimmed and sliced
Carrot 1 medium, peeled and grated
Pinhead or coarse oatmeal 100g (3½oz), toasted
Cooked red lentils 100g (3½oz)
Cooked pearl barley 100g (3½oz)
Grated nutmeg ¼ tsp
Dried sage 1 tsp
Vegetable suet 65g (2½oz)
Mashed potatoes, swede and fried sage leaves to serve (optional)

1 Heat oil in a frying pan and stir fry mushrooms, leek and carrot for 5 minutes. Reduce the heat, cover with a lid and cook gently for 5 minutes until tender. Transfer vegetables and juices to a large bowl and leave to cool.
2 Lightly grease 8 muffin tins. Add remaining ingredients and seasoning to cooled vegetables and stir well to make a slightly soft mixture.
3 Divide mixture between tins, and press each portion down firmly with the back of a spoon. The tins should be very full. Cover and chill for at least 2 hours to firm up.
4 Preheat oven to 200°C/180°fan/Gas 6. Cover tins with foil and bake for 30 minutes. Remove foil and bake for a further 15 minutes until golden and crisp on top. Stand for 5 minutes before turning onto serving plates to serve with mashed potatoes and swede. Garnish with fried sage leaves, if you like.

Serves 4 • Time 1½ hrs plus cooling & chilling
Calories 424 • Fibre 5.9g • Salt 0.5g • Sugar 0g
Fat 16.7g of which 6.1g is saturated

30 Monday

31 Tuesday

1 Wednesday FEBRUARY

2 Thursday

3 Friday

REMINDERS

Saturday 4

Sunday 5
Septuagesima Sunday
○ Full moon

BLOOD ORANGE & GINGER CURD

Blood oranges 4, grated zest and juice
Ginger 4cm (1½in) piece, peeled and grated
Caster sugar 150g (5oz)
Eggs 2 large, plus 2 extra yolks, beaten
Butter 125g (4½oz), chopped

1 Put orange zest, 200ml (7fl oz) juice, grated ginger, sugar, eggs and yolks, and butter in a heatproof bowl and lightly whisk to combine.
2 Bring a large pan of water to simmer and place bowl over the pan, not allowing the bottom to touch the water. Stir mixture frequently for 20-25 minutes until it thickens and coats the back of a spoon. Remove from the heat and pour through a sieve into a jug.
3 Pour curd into a sterilised jar, cool fully then cover with the lid. It will keep in the fridge for 2-3 weeks.
TIPS Serve with warm Scotch pancakes and Greek yogurt for a lovely brunch. Mix leftover egg whites with herbs and cheese, spoon onto fish fillets and bake.

Makes 450ml (16fl oz) • **Time 45 mins plus cooling**
Calories 41 • Fibre 0.1g • Salt 0.1g • Sugar 4g
Fat 2.6g of which 1.5g is saturated

6 Monday

7 Tuesday

8 Wednesday

9 Thursday

10 Friday

REMINDERS

Saturday 11

Sunday 12

MICROWAVE BACON & EGGS IN A MUG

Smoked back bacon rashers 2
Butter 1 tsp
Button mushrooms 25g (1oz), washed and sliced
Eggs 2 medium, beaten
Semi-skimmed milk 1 tbsp
Cherry tomatoes 6, halved
Toast to serve (optional)

1 Cut bacon in short snips along the fat side at regular intervals to help keep bacon flat during cooking. Place on a microwave-safe plate, cover loosely with a sheet of kitchen paper and cook on a high setting for 1½ minutes or until cooked. Drain fat and cut into small pieces.
2 Put butter in a large microwave-safe mug (at least 350ml/12fl oz) and cook on a high setting for 45 seconds or until melted. Stir in mushrooms, cover loosely and cook on a high setting for 2 minutes.
3 Mix eggs and milk together; season to taste.
4 Stir bacon and tomatoes into the mushrooms. Pour over egg mixture and cook on a high setting for 3 minutes until just set. Cover and rest for 5 minutes to cook through in the centre before serving with toast, if using.
TIPS The recipe uses a 900W microwave – adjust cooking times accordingly depending on your microwave. Make sure mugs are microwave-proof and take care when removing as the handles will be hot.

Serves 1 • **Time 20 mins**
Calories 499 • Fibre 2.1g • Salt 3.3g • Sugar 0g
Fat 38.9g of which 16.9g is saturated

13 Monday
☾ Last quarter

14 Tuesday
St Valentine's Day

15 Wednesday

16 Thursday

17 Friday

REMINDERS

Saturday 18

Sunday 19
Quinquagesima Sunday

MOCHA MATCHMAKER MARTINI

Chocolate or orange Matchmakers 16
Double cream 50ml (1½fl oz)
Chocolate cream liqueur 100ml (3½fl oz)
Vodka 75ml (2½fl oz)
Cold espresso 50ml (1½fl oz)
Ice to serve

1 Chop 12 chocolate or orange Matchmakers very finely, reserving 2 tbsp on a plate to decorate rims of the glasses.
2 Heat cream and chopped Matchmakers in a pan and whisk to a smooth ganache. Cool slightly to thicken then put in a piping bag.
3 Pipe a spiral shape around the inside of the glasses and a circle onto a plate. Dip the rim into the ganache circle and then into the reserved chocolate pieces.
4 Put chocolate liqueur, vodka and espresso in a cocktail shaker filled with ice and shake well.
5 Pour into the prepared glasses and garnish with the remaining Matchmakers.

Serves 2 • Time 20 mins
Calories 486 • Fibre 0.7g • Salt 0.1g • Sugar 36.4g
Fat 19.8g of which 12g is saturated

20 Monday
● New moon

21 Tuesday
Shrove Tuesday

22 Wednesday
Ash Wednesday

23 Thursday

24 Friday

REMINDERS

Saturday 25

Sunday 26
Quadragesima Sunday

CREAMY LEMON CRÊPE LAYER CAKE

Plain flour 125g (4½oz), sieved
Caster sugar 1 tbsp
Milk 350ml (12fl oz)
Eggs 2 large
Melted butter 1 tbsp, plus extra for frying
Mascarpone 250g (9oz)
Icing sugar 2 tbsp
Double cream 450ml (16fl oz)
Lemon 1, zest only
Lemon curd 225g (8oz)

1 Stir together flour, sugar and a pinch of salt in a bowl. Whisk together milk, eggs and 1 tbsp melted butter in another bowl then gradually pour into the dry ingredients, whisking to a smooth batter.
2 Heat a knob of butter in an 18cm (7in) frying pan and pour in a little batter, swirling the pan to cover base in an even layer. Cook for 1 minute each side until golden. Transfer to a plate and repeat until you have about 10 pancakes. Leave to cool, interleaved with baking paper.
3 Whisk together mascarpone, icing sugar, double cream and most of lemon zest to a soft cream. Swirl through 200g (7oz) lemon curd.
4 Place one pancake in the base of an 18cm (7in) loose-bottomed cake tin and spread evenly with 3 tbsp of the creamy mixture. Top with another pancake and repeat the stacking. Swirl remaining cream on top, then transfer to the fridge for at least 1 hour.
5 Drizzle over remaining lemon curd and scatter with remaining lemon zest just before serving.

Serves 10-12 • 45 mins plus cooling & chilling
Calories 496 • Fibre 0.6g • Salt 0.2g • Sugar 20.7g
Fat 39.3g of which 24.2g is saturated

27 Monday
) First quarter

28 Tuesday

1 Wednesday MARCH
St David's Day

2 Thursday

3 Friday

REMINDERS

Saturday 4

Sunday 5

HERBY LAMB & BEAN SOUP

Lean boneless lamb neck fillet or shoulder 375g (13oz), cut into 2.5cm (1in) cubes
Ground cumin 2 tsp
Rapeseed or olive oil 2 tbsp
Onions 2, peeled and finely chopped
Garlic 2 cloves, peeled and finely chopped
Tomato purée 2 tbsp
Hot lamb stock 600ml (1 pint)
Fresh rosemary 1 large sprig, leaves chopped
Fresh thyme 4 sprigs, leaves chopped
Butter beans or cannellini beans 400g tin, drained
Crusty bread to serve (optional)

1 Season lamb and dust with cumin. Heat oil in a large pan and brown lamb for 4-5 minutes. Add onions, garlic and tomato purée and cook for 1-2 minutes. Add stock, rosemary and half the thyme leaves.
2 Bring to the boil, then cover, reduce the heat and cook for 1½-2 hours, or until meat is tender. Add beans 20 minutes before the end of the cooking time.
3 Garnish with remaining thyme leaves and serve with crusty bread, if you like.

Serves 4 • **Time 2¼ hrs**
Calories 311 • Fibre 9.2g • Salt 1.3g • Sugar 0g
Fat 14.2g of which 3.9g is saturated

6 Monday

7 Tuesday

○ Full moon

8 Wednesday

9 Thursday

10 Friday

REMINDERS

Saturday 11

Sunday 12

SPICED CAULIFLOWER WEDGES WITH LENTIL & RICE PILAF

Cauliflower ½ medium, protruding stalk trimmed only
Vegetable oil 2 tbsp
Red onion 1 medium, peeled and sliced
Garlic 2 cloves, peeled and crushed
Red chilli 1, deseeded and chopped
Medium curry paste 1 tsp
Cooked lentils 250g pack
Cooked basmati rice 250g pack
Black onion (nigella) seeds 1½ tsp
Salted cashews 25g (1oz), crushed
Salad and fresh coriander leaves to serve (optional)

1 Discard any damaged outer leaves then slice cauliflower, remaining leaves included, into 4 wedges.
2 Bring a pan of water to the boil and gently poach cauli wedges for 6-7 minutes, covered, until almost cooked. Carefully drain and blot with kitchen paper; cool.
3 Heat 1 tbsp oil in a frying pan and fry onion, garlic and half the chilli for 5 minutes, stirring, then reduce the heat, cover and cook for 10 minutes until tender. Set aside.
4 Mix remaining oil with curry paste and brush half over tops of cauliflower wedges; season to taste. Heat the frying pan, place cauli wedges in the pan, oiled-side down, reduce heat and cook for 2-3 minutes until golden. Brush tops with remaining curried oil, flip and cook for 2-3 minutes more. Drain and keep warm.
5 In the same pan, add cooked onion mix, and lentils, rice and nigella seeds. Cook, stirring, for 4-5 minutes.
6 Pile onto warm serving plates, top with cauliflower and sprinkle with cashews and remaining chilli. Serve with salad and fresh coriander leaves, if liked.

Serves 2 • Time 1 hr plus cooling
Calories 567 • Fibre 13.2g • Salt 0.5g • Sugar 0g
Fat 22.4g of which 2.5g is saturated

13 Monday
Commonwealth Day

14 Tuesday

15 Wednesday
☾ Last quarter

16 Thursday

17 Friday
St Patrick's Day
Bank Holiday, Northern Ireland

REMINDERS

Saturday 18

Sunday 19
Mothering Sunday
Fourth Sunday in Lent

CHOCOLATE MARMALADE CAKE

Lightly salted butter 175g (6oz), softened, plus extra for greasing
Golden caster sugar 175g (6oz)
Eggs 3 medium
Plain flour 200g (7oz)
Orange 2 small, finely grated zest and juice
Dark chocolate chunks 150g (5oz)
Thick cut marmalade 75g (3oz)
Cocoa powder 25g (1oz)
Baking powder 1½ tsp
Icing sugar 110g (4oz)
Chocolate curls and chopped mixed peel to decorate (optional)

1 Preheat oven to 180°C/160°fan/Gas 4. Grease and triple-line a deep 18cm (7in) round cake tin.
2 Beat butter and caster sugar together for 2-3 minutes until light and fluffy. Beat in eggs one at a time, adding 1 tbsp flour with each, then whisk in zest and juice from 1 orange.
3 Add chocolate and marmalade and sift remaining flour, cocoa powder and baking powder on top. Gently fold dry ingredients into mixture then spoon into prepared tin and smooth top.
4 Bake for 1-1¼ hours until firm to touch and a skewer comes out clean. Cool in tin for 5 minutes then turn out onto a wire rack to cool completely.
5 To decorate, sift icing sugar into a bowl and add enough orange juice (about 1 tbsp) to make a smooth, spreadable icing. Spread over top of cake, allowing it to drip over the sides. Decorate with remaining orange zest, shaved chocolate curls and mixed peel, if liked.

Serves 10 • Time 1½ hrs plus cooling
Calories 439 • Fibre 1.8g • Salt 0.6g • Sugar 45.2g
Fat 20.8g of which 12.4g is saturated

20 Monday

Vernal equinox
Spring begins

21 Tuesday

● New moon

22 Wednesday

23 Thursday

24 Friday

REMINDERS

Saturday 25

Don't forget to put your clocks forward 1 hour tonight
(t.b.c. dependent on Government ruling)

Sunday 26

TERIYAKI SALMON STIR-FRY WITH WASABI NOODLES

Udon noodles ½ x 200g pack
Salmon fillets 2
Teriyaki sauce 4 tbsp
Sesame seeds 2 tsp
Sunflower oil 2 tbsp
Stir-fry vegetables 300g pack
Wasabi powder 1 tsp
Soy sauce 1 tbsp

1 Cook noodles according to packet instructions; drain well. Meanwhile, coat salmon fillets with half the teriyaki sauce.
2 Heat a wok or frying pan and toast sesame seeds briefly until lightly golden, then tip onto a small plate.
3 Heat half the oil in the pan and cook salmon for 2–3 minutes each side. Remove from the pan.
4 Heat remaining oil in the pan, add vegetables and stir-fry for 2–3 minutes until softened, then stir in remaining teriyaki sauce. Flake cooked salmon into the pan.
5 Stir wasabi powder into soy sauce, then stir into noodles. Divide noodles between two plates, top with salmon and vegetables and sprinkle toasted sesame seeds over to serve.

Serves 2 • Time 20 mins
Calories 571 • Fibre 2.5g • Salt 2.3g • Sugar 17.8g
Fat 35.1g of which 5.2g is saturated

27 Monday

28 Tuesday

29 Wednesday

) First quarter

30 Thursday

31 Friday

REMINDERS

Saturday 1

Sunday 2
Palm Sunday

ASPARAGUS, SHALLOT & MOZZARELLA FOCACCIA

Strong bread flour 500g (1lb 2oz)
Fast-action dried yeast 7g sachet
Fine salt 2 tsp
Olive oil 3 tbsp, plus extra for oiling
Echalion shallots 2, peeled and sliced
Fresh green pesto 2 tbsp
Buffalo mozzarella 200g (7oz), torn into pieces
British asparagus spears 150g (5oz), trimmed
Flaky sea salt 1 tsp

1 In a mixing bowl combine flour, yeast and fine salt and make a well in the middle. Add 2 tbsp olive oil and around 350ml (12fl oz) lukewarm water and stir to form a sticky dough.
2 Turn dough out onto a floured surface and knead for 5-10 minutes until soft and springy. Place in a clean, oiled bowl and leave covered with a tea towel to rise for 1 hour.
3 Oil a baking tin (about 25x35cm/10x14in), shape dough into tin and leave, covered, for another 30-40 minutes.
4 Preheat oven to 220°C/200°fan/Gas 7. Meanwhile, in a frying pan, heat 1 tbsp oil and gently fry shallots for 5 minutes until softened.
5 Spread dough with pesto and shallots then make holes in dough with your fingers and push in pieces of mozzarella. Bake for 20 minutes. Remove from oven and push asparagus spears into hot dough, sprinkle with sea salt and return to oven for a further 10 minutes or until cheese is bubbling.

Serves 8-10 • **Time 50 mins plus rising**
Calories 291 • Fibre 2.2g • Salt 1.8g • Sugar 0g
Fat 11g of which 3.8g is saturated

3 Monday

4 Tuesday

5 Wednesday

6 Thursday

○ Full moon

7 Friday

Good Friday
Bank Holiday, UK

REMINDERS

Saturday 8

Sunday 9
Easter Day

CULLEN SKINK BAKE

Charlotte potatoes 300g (11oz), scrubbed
Leek 1 large, trimmed and washed
Vegetable oil 4 tsp
Smoked haddock 2 x 150g (5oz) fillets
Butter 15g (½oz)
Bay leaves 3
Reduced-fat soft cheese with garlic and herbs 75g (3oz)
Single cream 75ml (2½fl oz)
Chopped fresh chives 2 tbsp
Steamed green vegetables to serve (optional)

1 Preheat oven to 200°C/180°fan/Gas 6. Cut potatoes into chunks about 2cm (¾in) thick and place in a bowl. Cut leek into 1cm (½in) thick pieces and mix into potatoes along with oil; season. Spread evenly in a shallow tin or baking dish, cover with foil and bake for 30 minutes, then remove foil and nestle haddock among vegetables.
2 Dot fish with butter, season with black pepper and place a bay leaf on each fillet. Bake, uncovered, for 15-20 minutes until fish is cooked through and veg are tender.
3 Towards the end of cooking, put soft cheese in a small saucepan with cream and remaining bay leaf. Heat very gently, stirring, without boiling, until melted and hot. Stir in half the chopped chives, season to taste and keep warm.
4 To serve, discard bay leaves, drain fish and vegetables and pile onto warm serving plates. Drizzle over cream sauce and scatter with remaining chives. Serve with freshly cooked green vegetables, if liked.
TIP This recipe also works well with salmon or trout fillets or any white fish fillet.

Serves 2 • Time 1 hr 10 mins
Calories 622 • Fibre 5.2g • Salt 3g • Sugar 0g
Fat 38g of which 11.1 g is saturated

10 Monday

Easter Monday
Bank Holiday, England, Wales, Northern Ireland

11 Tuesday

12 Wednesday

13 Thursday

☾ Last quarter

14 Friday

REMINDERS

Saturday 15

Sunday 16
Low Sunday

SAVOURY HOT CROSS BUNS

White bread mix 500g pack
Freshly grated vegetarian hard cheese 75g (3oz)
Sultanas 50g (2oz)
Onion chutney 50g (2oz)
Egg 1 medium, beaten
Square cheese slices 3
Butter, cheese & extra chutney to serve (optional)

1 Put bread mix in a bowl and stir in cheese and sultanas. Put chutney in a jug and make up to quantity of water in bread mix packet instructions. Stir into bread mix and mix, knead and rest according to packet instructions.
2 Divide dough into 12 and form each into a neat ball. Arrange on a lined baking tray, cover with a damp cloth or oiled clingfilm and leave to rise in a warm place for 30-40 minutes or until doubled in size.
3 Preheat oven to 230°C/210°fan/Gas 8. Uncover buns, brush with egg and bake for 18-20 minutes until richly golden and hollow-sounding when you tap the base.
4 While buns are baking, cut each cheese slice into 8 strips. As soon as buns are baked, arrange 2 strips of cheese on top of each bun in the shape of a cross – the cheese should melt in place – then transfer buns to a wire rack to cool completely.
5 Serve buns as they are with butter, cheese and chutney, or halve and grill to toast slightly.
TIPS You can use Parmesan in place of the vegetarian hard cheese if suitable. For a tomato twist, replace onion chutney with a tomato chutney and use chopped sundried tomatoes in place of the sultanas.

Makes 12 • Time 40 minutes plus resting & rising
Calories 210 • Fibre 1g • Salt 0.7g • Sugar 0g
Fat 4.5g of which 2.4g is saturated

17 Monday

18 Tuesday

19 Wednesday

20 Thursday

● New moon

21 Friday

REMINDERS

Saturday 22

Sunday 23
St George's Day

RHUBARB & CUSTARD ETON MESS

Fresh rhubarb 200g (7oz), trimmed
Vanilla pod ½, split
Caster sugar 2 tbsp
Whipping cream 75ml (2½fl oz)
Vanilla custard 4 tbsp
Meringue nests 2, crushed
Shortbread fingers 2, lightly crumbled

1 Slice rhubarb into 2.5cm (1in) lengths and place in a saucepan with vanilla, sugar and 2 tbsp water. Heat until steaming, then cover and cook gently for 7-8 minutes until just tender. Leave to cool then chill until required.
2 To serve, whip cream to soft peaks, then whisk in custard. Discard vanilla pod from the rhubarb. Layer in sundae glasses or tall tumblers with custard cream, crushed meringue and shortbread. Serve immediately.
TIPS Using real vanilla in this recipe gives a delicious sweet spice to the rhubarb, but you can use a good-quality vanilla extract instead. Use between ½ and 1 tsp depending on the strength. For a no-cook version of this recipe, try combining chopped strawberries with raspberries and blueberries for a berry dessert. Chopped peaches and nectarines are a good choice when in season, either cooked or fresh.

Serves 2 • Time 20 mins plus cooling & chilling
Calories 353 • Fibre 2.2g • Salt 0.2g • Sugar 31.4g
Fat 20.1g of which 12.5g is saturated

24 Monday

25 Tuesday

26 Wednesday

27 Thursday

) First quarter

28 Friday

REMINDERS

Saturday 29

Sunday 30

LOADED PULLED JACKFRUIT NACHOS

Olive oil 2 tbsp
Spring onions 6, thinly sliced
Jackfruit 2 x 420g tins, drained and chopped
Chipotle paste 2 tbsp
Lightly salted tortilla chips 200g pack
Cherry tomatoes 150g (5oz), halved
Vegan cheese 150g (5oz), grated
Ripe avocado 1 large, peeled and destoned
Lime 1, juice only
Fresh coriander leaves 15g (½oz), chopped
Tomato salsa and creamy oat fraîche to serve (optional)

1 Heat oil in a pan and fry spring onions for 1-2 minutes. Tip in chopped jackfruit, 250ml (8½fl oz) water and chipotle paste and mix together. Cover and cook for 20-25 minutes until jackfruit is tender and pulls apart; season.
2 Preheat oven to 200°C/180°fan/Gas 6. Evenly spread tortilla chips in a large, shallow ovenproof dish. Top with jackfruit mixture, tomatoes and grated vegan cheese, then bake for 15-20 minutes until golden and cheese is melted.
3 Meanwhile, mash together avocado, lime juice and small handful of chopped coriander; season to taste. Serve alongside nachos with tomato salsa, creamy oat fraîche and remaining coriander scattered over, if liked.

Serves 4 • **Time 50 mins**
Calories 650 • Fibre 5g • Salt 1.5g • Sugar 0g
Fat 37.7g of which 11.4g is saturated

1 Monday
Bank Holiday, UK

2 Tuesday

3 Wednesday

4 Thursday

5 Friday
○ Full moon

REMINDERS

Saturday 6

Sunday 7

LIQUORICE ALLSORTS PASTEL CUPCAKES

Butter 275g (10oz), softened
Golden caster sugar 150g (5oz)
Eggs 2 large, beaten
Self-raising flour 150g (5oz)
Chinese 5-spice 1 tsp
Orange 1 small, finely grated zest and juice
Icing sugar 250g (9oz), sieved
Pink food colouring
Liquorice Allsorts to decorate

1 Preheat oven to 180°C/160°fan/Gas 4. Line a 12-hole cupcake tin with paper cases. Whisk together 150g (5oz) butter and caster sugar until pale and fluffy then gradually whisk in beaten eggs. Sieve in flour and spice, folding in carefully. Stir in orange juice and zest to loosen the mixture.
2 Divide mixture between the cases and bake for 18-20 minutes until risen and lightly golden. Leave to cool on a wire rack.
3 In a bowl whisk remaining butter for 1-2 minutes until light and creamy, then gradually whisk in icing sugar and pink colouring to make a smooth, soft icing. Pipe or spread icing onto each cake and decorate each with a few Liquorice Allsorts.
TIP For a vegetarian version, omit the pink food colouring and use vegan sweets in place of the Liquorice Allsorts.

Serves 12 • Time 30 mins
Calories 374 • Fibre 0.6g • Salt 0.2g • Sugar 38.2g
Fat 20g of which 12.4g is saturated

8 Monday

9 Tuesday

10 Wednesday

11 Thursday

12 Friday
☾ Last quarter

REMINDERS

Saturday 13

Sunday 14
Rogation Sunday

SAUSAGE & LEEK SUPPER

Potatoes 700g (1lb 9oz), peeled and sliced
Butter 25g (1oz)
Sausages with herbs 450g (1lb), sliced
Onion 1, peeled and sliced
Leeks 4, washed and sliced
Plain flour 40g (1½oz)
Milk 450ml (16fl oz)
Smoked Cheddar cheese 110g (4oz), grated
Fresh breadcrumbs 25g (1oz)

1 Preheat oven to 200°C/180°fan/Gas 6. Meanwhile, cook potatoes in boiling salted water for 4-5 minutes until just tender. Drain.
2 While potatoes are cooking, melt butter in a large pan, add sliced sausage and cook for 5 minutes. Add onion and leeks and cook for a further 5 minutes.
3 Add flour, cook for 1 minute, then gradually add milk and 75g (3oz) cheese, stirring. Bring to the boil then simmer for 1-2 minutes, stirring continuously.
4 Transfer to a 2 litre (3½ pint) ovenproof dish, arrange potato slices on top, sprinkle with breadcrumbs and remaining cheese and bake for 20-30 minutes until browned. Serve hot.
TIP Keep an eye on the potato slices as you cook them in boiling water. They should be only just tender as they will also cook when the dish goes into the oven. Otherwise, it will be difficult to arrange them on the top.

Serves 6 • **Time 50 mins**
Calories 529 • Fibre 7g • Salt 1.4g • Sugar 0g
Fat 30.4g of which 14g is saturated

15 Monday

16 Tuesday

17 Wednesday

18 Thursday

Ascension Day
Holy Thursday

19 Friday

● New moon

REMINDERS

Saturday 20

Sunday 21

PEA & BASIL SOUP WITH CHORIZO TOASTS

Chorizo 40g (1½oz), chopped
Petits pois 300g (11oz)
Vegetable stock 450ml (¾ pint)
Baguette or small rustic loaf 2-4 slices
Cheddar cheese 25g (1oz)
Fresh chopped basil 2 tbsp
Extra-virgin olive oil 2 tsp, to serve (optional)

1 In a large pan fry 25g (1oz) chorizo for 2-4 minutes until its oil is released. Reduce heat, add petits pois and stir for 2 minutes. Pour in stock, bring to the boil then simmer for 10 minutes.

2 Meanwhile, preheat grill and lightly toast bread on one side. Mix cheese with remaining chorizo and pile onto untoasted side of the bread. Grill for 4-7 minutes until cheese is melted and bubbling.

3 Add basil to the soup. Whizz with a stick blender until smooth. Serve in warm bowls, with a swirl of olive oil, if liked, and with chorizo toasts alongside.

TIP For a vegetarian version, omit chorizo and fry peas in butter. Serve with grilled cheese on toast, without the chorizo.

Serves 2 • Time 20 mins
Calories 413 • Fibre 8.9g • Salt 4.1g • Sugar 0g
Fat 23.9g of which 6.8g is saturated

22 Monday

23 Tuesday

24 Wednesday

25 Thursday

26 Friday

REMINDERS

Saturday 27

) First quarter

Sunday 28

Whit Sunday

Pentecost

HERBY CHICKEN TRAYBAKE

Boneless, skinless chicken thighs 250g (9oz)
Balsamic vinegar 1 tbsp
Garlic 1 clove, peeled and crushed
Sundried tomato paste 2 tbsp
Dried oregano 1 tsp
Olive oil 2 tbsp
Red onion 1 medium, peeled and chopped
Carrot 1 large, peeled and chopped
Celery stick 1, trimmed and chopped
Small ripe tomatoes 225g (8oz), quartered
Butter beans 400g tin, drained and rinsed
Fresh basil leaves, cooked pasta and olives to serve (optional)

1 Cut chicken into 2cm (¾in) thick pieces and place in a bowl; season. Mix in vinegar, garlic, tomato paste and oregano. Cover and chill for at least 2 hours, then thread loosely onto 2 long skewers. Mix 1 tsp oil with the marinade juices and set aside.
2 Preheat oven to 200°C/180°fan/Gas 6. Mix onion, carrot, celery and tomatoes together with remaining oil. Spread out on a lined baking tray, season and cover with foil. Bake for 20 minutes.
3 Uncover, stir veg, sit chicken skewers on top, brush with marinade juices and bake for 15 minutes more. Remove skewers, stir in beans, replace skewers opposite side up and cook for 10 minutes or until chicken is cooked through.
4 To serve, drain tray and divide veg and chicken between serving plates. Scatter with fresh basil and accompany with freshly cooked pasta and olives, if liked.

Serves 2 • Time 1 hr plus marinating
Calories 432 • Fibre 15.9g • Salt 1.3g • Sugar 0g
Fat 15.8g of which 2.8g is saturated

29 Monday
Bank Holiday, UK

30 Tuesday

31 Wednesday

1 Thursday JUNE

2 Friday

REMINDERS

Saturday 3

Sunday 4
Trinity Sunday
○ Full moon

STICKY TOFFEE PUDDING

Chopped dates 175g (6oz)
Bicarbonate of soda 1 tsp
Butter 160g (5½oz), softened
Soft light brown sugar 325g (11½oz)
Eggs 2 medium, beaten
Self-raising flour 175g (6oz)
Double cream 150ml (¼ pint)
Vanilla ice cream to serve (optional)

1 Preheat oven to 180°C/160°fan/Gas 4 and grease and line an 18cm (7in) square cake tin.
2 Put dates in a pan with 300ml (10fl oz) water and bring to the boil, then reduce the heat and simmer for 5 minutes, stirring occasionally. Remove pan from the heat, add bicarbonate of soda and leave to stand for 10 minutes.
3 Whisk 50g (2oz) butter and 175g (6oz) sugar in a bowl with an electric whisk until soft and pale. Gradually add eggs, whisking well after each addition, then fold in flour followed by date mixture. Spoon into tin and bake for 40-50 minutes until risen and firm to touch.
4 To make the sauce, put remaining butter and sugar into a pan with cream and heat gently until sugar has dissolved, then bring to the boil. Reduce heat and simmer for 1-2 minutes until combined into a toffee sauce.
5 Cut pudding into portions and serve with toffee sauce and a little vanilla ice cream, if you like.

Serves 8 • Time 1 hr 30 mins
Calories 548 • Fibre 2g • Salt 0.7g • Sugar 41.8g
Fat 28g of which 17.1g is saturated

5 Monday

6 Tuesday

7 Wednesday

8 Thursday
Corpus Christi

9 Friday

REMINDERS

Saturday 10

(Last quarter

Sunday 11

BRIE & CHIVE OMELETTE

Eggs 4
Fresh chives small bunch
Butter 25g (½oz)
Brie or Camembert 110g (4oz)
Potato wedges and mixed salad
to serve (optional)

1 Break eggs into a bowl and beat until just mixed. Season and snip in chives with scissors (aiming for about 4 tbsp chopped chives).
2 Heat a small frying pan, add half the butter and when sizzling, shake to swirl butter around. Pour half the beaten eggs into the pan. Move pan around so eggs are spread out evenly and cook for 1-2 minutes until omelette is beginning to set.
3 Snip cheese with scissors in rough cubes over omelette. Leave on a low heat for 30 seconds, then, using a spatula, fold one-third of omelette to the middle, then the other third over and slide onto a plate. Repeat for a second omelette.
4 Serve with potato wedges and mixed salad, if you like.
TIP For a vegetarian version, make sure to use cheeses produced without animal rennet.

Serves 2 • Time 10 mins
Calories 415 • Fibre 0.2g • Salt 1.2g • Sugar 0g
Fat 35.3g of which 19.1g is saturated

12 Monday

13 Tuesday

14 Wednesday

15 Thursday

16 Friday

REMINDERS

Saturday 17

Sunday 18

Father's Day

● New moon

HOMEMADE DONER KEBAB

Lean minced lamb 400g (14oz)
Ground cumin ½ tsp
Ground coriander ½ tsp
Dried oregano ½ tsp
Dried onion granules ½ tsp
Dried garlic granules ½ tsp
Large pitta breads 4
Little Gem lettuce 1, shredded
Ripe tomatoes 2, sliced
Cucumber ¼, sliced
Chilli sauce and hummus to serve (optional)

1 Preheat oven to 200°C/180°fan/Gas 6. Lightly grease a 500g (1lb 2oz) loaf tin. Mix lamb, spices, and granules thoroughly, season generously and press firmly into tin. Bake for 30 minutes then cover and rest for 10 minutes.
2 Meanwhile, heat or toast pittas according to packet instructions, and slice down the length of each to open. Keep warm.
3 To serve, drain and reserve cooking juices from loaf tin. Remove loaf from the tin and slice lengthways into 12 long strips. Fill pittas with salad ingredients and slices of loaf. Serve stuffed pittas warm drizzled with chilli sauce and with hummus alongside, if liked.
TIP If you want to serve 1 or 2 pittas, the reserved meat can be cooled and frozen for later use. Keep the juices and spoon over the lamb slices before freezing to help prevent the meat from drying out when you reheat it.

Makes 4 • Time 45 mins
Calories 387 • Fibre 1.9g • Salt 1g • Sugar 0.8g
Fat 14.5g of which 6.4g is saturated

19 Monday

20 Tuesday

21 Wednesday

Summer solstice
Summer begins

22 Thursday

23 Friday

REMINDERS

Saturday 24

Sunday 25

PORK MEDALLIONS RAMEN

Rapeseed or olive oil 1 tsp
Pork loin medallions 2, trimmed of fat
Teriyaki sauce 1 tbsp
Vegetable stock 1 litre (1¾ pints)
Hot chilli sauce 2 tsp or to taste
Shiitake or chestnut mushrooms 125g (4½oz), wiped and sliced
Pak choi 200g (7oz), sliced
Red pepper 1, deseeded and sliced
Flat rice noodles 110g (4oz)
Beansprouts 110g (4oz)
Red chilli 1, deseeded and finely sliced (optional)
Fresh coriander 4 sprigs (optional)

1 Heat oil in a nonstick frying pan, add pork and cook for 7 minutes, turning once. Add teriyaki sauce and 3 tbsp water; cook for a further 2 minutes or until juices run clear.
2 Meanwhile, add stock to a large pan with chilli sauce and bring to the boil, then reduce the heat and simmer for 2 minutes.
3 Add mushrooms, pak choi, pepper, noodles and beansprouts to chilli broth, cover and simmer for 4 minutes until noodles and vegetables are tender.
4 Slice pork thinly. Divide noodles and vegetables between 2 bowls and ladle over broth. Top each with the pork strips, chilli and coriander, if using. Serve immediately.

Serves 2 • Time 20 mins
Calories 353 • Fibre 5.2g • Salt 3.1g • Sugar 2.3g
Fat 13.1g of which 2.5g is saturated

26 Monday

) First quarter

27 Tuesday

28 Wednesday

29 Thursday

30 Friday

REMINDERS

Saturday 1

Sunday 2

TUNA STEAK & MAYO SANDWICH

Red pepper 1 small, deseeded and chopped
Spring onions 2, trimmed and finely chopped
Cooked sweetcorn 110g (4oz)
White wine vinegar 1 tbsp
Clear honey 1 tsp
Fresh yellowfin tuna 2 x 125g (4½oz) steaks
Olive oil 1 tbsp
Mayonnaise 2 tbsp
White bread 4 thick slices
Crisp salad leaves a handful

1 Put red pepper, spring onions and sweetcorn in a bowl. Stir in vinegar and honey, season to taste and set aside until ready to serve.
2 Season tuna on both sides. Heat oil in a frying pan over a medium heat and cook tuna for 2-3 minutes until lightly browned. Turn over and cook for a further 2-3 minutes or until cooked to your liking.
3 Spread a little mayonnaise on two slices of bread, top with a few salad leaves and a tuna steak. Spoon over more mayonnaise and a little of the sweetcorn mixture. Sandwich together with remaining bread. Serve immediately with remaining sweetcorn relish on the side.

Serves 2 • Time 15 mins
Calories 511 • Fibre 3.7g • Salt 3.3g • Sugar 7.2g
Fat 26.3g of which 2.7g is saturated

3 Monday

○ Full moon

4 Tuesday

5 Wednesday

6 Thursday

7 Friday

REMINDERS

Saturday 8

Sunday 9

TROPICAL MORNING JUICE

Oranges 2
Carrot 1, peeled and sliced
Grated root ginger 1 tsp
Tropical fruit mix 225g (8oz), frozen or fresh
Lime 1, juice from ½, other ½ cut into 4 wedges

1 Cut peel from oranges then cut into segments, catching the juice.
2 Put fruit and juice into a blender with carrot, ginger, tropical fruit mix, lime juice and 150ml (¼ pint) cold water. Whizz until smooth.
3 Pour into four tumblers and squeeze in extra juice from lime wedges to taste.
TIPS Segment oranges the night before and keep in the fridge to save time in the morning. Alternatively, you can blend mixture the night before and keep in the fridge overnight; simply stir before serving.

Serves 4 • Time 10 mins
Calories 60 • Fibre 3.2g • Salt 0g • Sugar 7.8g
Fat 0.4g of which 0.1g is saturated

10 Monday
(Last quarter

11 Tuesday

12 Wednesday
Bank Holiday, Northern Ireland

13 Thursday

14 Friday

REMINDERS

Saturday 15

Sunday 16

ASIAN STEAK & CASHEW STIR-FRY

Frying steak 300g (11oz)
Chinese five spice powder ½ tsp
Soy sauce 1 tbsp
Savoy cabbage 1 small, cored and finely shredded
Cashew nuts 50g (2oz)
Vegetable oil 4 tsp
Root ginger 2.5cm (1in) piece, unpeeled, grated
Garlic 1 clove, peeled and grated
Shallot 1, peeled and sliced
Dried chilli flakes ½–1 tsp
Thai fish sauce 1 tbsp
Lime 1, juice only
Chopped coriander and mint leaves 25g (1oz)

1 Put steak on a plate and sprinkle with five spice powder then drizzle with soy sauce.
2 Place cabbage into a colander over a large saucepan and pour a kettleful of boiling water over it. Drain.
3 Heat a wok or large frying pan and toast cashews until just turning brown. Set aside.
4 Heat 2 teaspoons of oil in the wok over a high heat. Add steak, reserving marinade. Sear 1 minute on each side then keep warm.
5 Add remaining oil along with ginger, garlic, shallot and chilli flakes. Stir-fry for 30 seconds then add cabbage and stir-fry for 3 minutes. Pour in marinade along with fish sauce, lime juice and half the herbs.
6 Spoon onto a serving platter. Cut steak into strips and arrange it on top, spooning on the meat juices. Scatter with cashews and remaining herbs.

Serves 4 • Time 20 mins
Calories 303 • Fibre 3.2g • Salt 0.8g • Sugar 0g
Fat 21.4g of which 3.4g is saturated

17 Monday

● New moon

18 Tuesday

19 Wednesday

20 Thursday

21 Friday

REMINDERS

Saturday 22

Sunday 23

BAKED SALMON WITH WATERCRESS SAUCE

Skinless salmon fillets 4, each approx. 150g (5oz),
Lemon ½, juice only
Fresh dill 15g (½oz)
Butter 20g (¾oz)
Cucumber ½, thinly sliced
White wine vinegar 2 tbsp
Caster sugar 1 tsp
Chives 15g (½oz), finely snipped
Chopped watercress 2 tbsp, plus sprigs to garnish
Soft cheese 110g (4oz)
Light mayonnaise 2 tbsp
Steamed new potatoes to serve (optional)

1 Preheat oven to 180°C/160°fan/Gas 4. Line a large baking tray with foil.
2 Place salmon fillets on the foil, drizzle with lemon juice, sprinkle with a little torn dill, dot with butter and season with salt and pepper. Enclose salmon in the foil then bake for 25-30 minutes or until fish flakes easily.
3 Meanwhile, add cucumber slices to a bowl with vinegar, sugar and a little salt and pepper. Reserve a few more dill sprigs for garnish, chop the rest and add half to the cucumber and remainder to a second bowl. Add half the chives to the cucumber and the rest to the second bowl.
4 Add chopped watercress, soft cheese and mayonnaise to the bowl of herbs and stir together until well mixed.
5 Spoon cucumber onto a large shallow platter. Arrange salmon on top then garnish with dill. Serve with the watercress sauce and new potatoes, if using.

Serves 4 • Time 40 mins
Calories 465 • Fibre ?g • Salt ?g • Sugar ?g
Fat 35g of which 11g is saturated

24 Monday
Remember to test your smoke alarms.

25 Tuesday
☽ First quarter

26 Wednesday

27 Thursday

28 Friday

REMINDERS

Saturday 29

Sunday 30

ALMOND BERRY FINGERS

Ground almonds 200g (7oz)
Bicarbonate of soda ½ tsp
Lemon 1, finely grated zest and 2 tsp juice
Vanilla extract 1 tsp
Maple syrup 2 tbsp
Eggs 3, beaten
Melted butter 3 tbsp
Strawberries 110g (4oz), hulled and halved or quartered if large
Blueberries 200g (7oz)
Flaked almonds 2 tbsp

1 Preheat oven to 180°C/160°fan/Gas 4. Line a 20cm (8in) square cake tin with baking paper.
2 Mix ground almonds, bicarbonate of soda, lemon zest and juice, vanilla and maple syrup in a large bowl. Add eggs, mix in well then add melted butter and mix until smooth. Pour mixture into tin, scatter with the strawberries and blueberries then the almonds.
3 Bake for 40 minutes until golden on top and firm to the touch. Leave in tin to cool, then cut into 10 fingers and serve warm or cold.

Makes 10 • Time 1 hr plus cooling
Calories 211 • Fibre 0.7g • Salt 0.2g • Sugar 3.5g
Fat 17.8g of which 4g is saturated

31 Monday

1 Tuesday AUGUST

○ Full moon

2 Wednesday

3 Thursday

4 Friday

REMINDERS

Saturday 5

Sunday 6

EDIBLE FLOWER RASPBERRY ICE POPS

Lime cordial 3 tbsp
Lemonade 250ml (9fl oz)
Raspberries 125g (4½oz), halved if large
Edible flowers such as borage, pansies, lavender or roses, washed and petals picked

1 In a jug mix cordial and lemonade, then chill for 1 hour in the fridge.
2 Divide raspberries and flowers in lolly moulds so they are evenly positioned in the mould.
3 Very slowly pour in lemonade cordial then position the sticks into the moulds, making sure raspberries and flowers are still evenly positioned. Transfer to freezer and leave to freeze overnight.
4 To serve, dip the moulds into hot water for a few seconds to remove.
TIP Use 50ml lolly moulds for this recipe.

Makes 6 • Time 15 mins plus chilling & overnight freezing
Calories 23 • Fibre 0.7g • Salt 0g • Sugar 4.6g
Fat 0.1g of which 0g is saturated

7 Monday

Bank Holiday, Scotland

8 Tuesday

(Last quarter

9 Wednesday

10 Thursday

11 Friday

REMINDERS

Saturday 12

Sunday 13

EGGY CAESAR CROSTINI

Little Gem lettuce 1, trimmed
Anchovies in oil 50g tin, drained and chopped
Freshly grated Parmesan cheese 2 tbsp
Caesar salad dressing 2 tbsp
Small ciabatta loaf 1
Garlic butter 25g (1oz), softened
Eggs 2 medium
Fresh basil a few leaves
Halved plum tomatoes to serve (optional)

1 Slice lettuce thinly and place in a bowl. Mix in anchovies, cheese and dressing. Set aside.
2 Slice ciabatta lengthways down the centre, and then in half again to make 4 pieces.
3 Preheat grill to hot and toast bread very lightly on the cut side for 1 minute. Spread with garlic butter and replace under grill for a few seconds more to melt the butter; keep warm.
4 Poach eggs in a pan of simmering water for 5 minutes then drain with a slotted spoon.
5 To serve, arrange toasted bread on serving plates and pile on the salad. Place eggs on top. Scatter with basil leaves and serve immediately. Accompany with halved plum tomatoes, if liked.
TIPS This recipe is best prepared just before cooking to enjoy the salad crisp and the bread and egg warm. If anchovies aren't to your taste, use flakes of tuna or some smoked salmon instead.

Serves 2 • Time 25 mins
Calories 593 • Fibre 2.4g • Salt 3.4g • Sugar 0g
Fat 44.6g of which 14.5g is saturated

14 Monday

15 Tuesday

16 Wednesday

● New moon

17 Thursday

18 Friday

REMINDERS

Saturday 19

Sunday 20

SMOKY RED PEPPER JELLY

Cooking apples 625g (1lb 6oz), chopped
Large red peppers 400g (14oz), halved, deseeded and finely chopped
Garlic 2 cloves, peeled and chopped
Large red chilli 1, washed and chopped
Bay leaves 2
Granulated sugar 625g (1lb 6oz)
Cider or white wine vinegar 50ml (1¾fl oz)
Smoked paprika 1 tsp
Salt ¾ tsp

1 Place apples in a large, non-reactive saucepan including seeds, core and skin. Add chopped peppers, garlic and chilli to the pan along with bay leaves.
2 Pour over 750ml (1¼ pints) water. Bring to the boil, cover and simmer gently for 30 minutes until soft and pulpy. Mash with a spoon and cool for 30 minutes.
3 If you have a jelly bag, suspend it over a non-reactive bowl or jug and ladle the contents of the saucepan into the bag. Alternatively, line a large nylon sieve with muslin and sit this over a similar bowl. Leave mixture to drip for at least 4 hours or overnight in a cool place.
4 Discard pulp. Pour juice into a large saucepan. Add sugar and vinegar, heat while gently stirring until the sugar dissolves, then turn up the heat and boil rapidly for 10 minutes until setting point is reached (105°C/221°F on a sugar thermometer). Spoon a little onto a cold plate – it is ready if it wrinkles when pushed with your finger.
5 Stir in paprika and salt then spoon into sterilised jars and seal tightly with non-corrosive lids. Leave to cool. Label and date. The jelly is ready to eat immediately. It will store in a cool, dry cupboard for at least 6 months.

Makes 900g (2lb) • 1 hr 20 mins plus cooling & straining
Calories 27 • Fibre 0.2g • Salt 0g • Sugar 6.2g
Fat 0g of which 0g is saturated

21 Monday

22 Tuesday

23 Wednesday

24 Thursday

☽ First quarter

25 Friday

REMINDERS

Saturday 26

Sunday 27

MASSAMAN CHICKEN WITH NUTTY GREEN BEANS

Skin-on chicken breasts 2
Thai curry paste 4 tsp
Thai sweet chilli sauce 4 tsp, plus extra to serve (optional)
Vegetable oil 2 tsp
Fine green beans 110g (4oz), trimmed
Lime 1, grated zest and juice from ½, other ½ cut into wedges
Roughly chopped salted roasted peanuts 1 tbsp
Noodles or new potatoes to serve (optional)

1 Place chicken breasts between two sheets of baking paper and use a rolling pin to flatten them to about 1cm (½in) thick. Mix curry paste with 2 tsp chilli sauce. Rub mixture over chicken and set aside at room temperature for 10 minutes.
2 Heat a griddle pan until very hot. Put chicken on the griddle and cook for 3 minutes then turn over and cook for another 3 minutes or until cooked through. Set aside on a warm plate.
3 Heat oil in a wok or large frying pan and when hot, add beans and stir-fry for 4 minutes until just tender and starting to char. Take off the heat, then add lime zest, juice and nuts.
4 Divide beans between two warm plates and drizzle with remaining chilli sauce. Add chicken and lime wedges. Serve with noodles or new potatoes, if you like, and extra sweet chilli sauce.

Serves 2 • Time 15 mins plus marinating
Calories 424 • Fibre 5.1g • Salt 1.8g • Sugar 2g
Fat 24.4g of which 2.1g is saturated

28 Monday

Bank Holiday, England, Wales, Northern Ireland

29 Tuesday

30 Wednesday

31 Thursday

○ Full moon

1 Friday SEPTEMBER

REMINDERS

Saturday 2

Sunday 3

BARBECUED GREEK SALAD FLATBREADS

Green pepper 1 small, halved and deseeded
Little Gem lettuce 1, trimmed and cut into 8 chunks
Large ripe tomato 1, cut into 8 wedges
Halloumi cheese 100g (3½oz), cut into 6 chunks
Olive oil 5 tsp
Clear honey 2 tsp
Concentrated mint sauce 1 tsp
Greek yogurt 75g (3oz)
Cucumber 50g (2oz), finely chopped
Small plain naans or similar flatbreads 2

1 Cut pepper into large chunks. Bring a pan of water to the boil and cook pepper for 5 minutes to soften. Drain and cool in cold running water. Pat dry and set aside.
2 Thread lettuce onto a long skewer, and pepper, tomato and cheese onto 2 more skewers. Cover and chill until ready to cook.
3 Mix oil, honey and mint sauce together; season to taste. Mix 1 tbsp into yogurt with cucumber. Cover and chill until ready to cook and serve.
4 Prepare and preheat barbecue. To cook, brush skewers with remaining dressing and cook over hot coals, turning to cook all over. The lettuce and breads take a few seconds; the veg and cheese need 1-2 minutes each side.
5 To serve, drain veg and cheese and remove from skewers. Pile on top of flatbreads. Serve immediately with cucumber and mint yogurt.

Serves 2 • **Time 30 mins plus cooling**
Calories 743 • Fibre 5.3g • Salt 3.5g • Sugar 11.4g
Fat 43.2g of which 14.7g is saturated

4 Monday

5 Tuesday

6 Wednesday

(Last quarter

7 Thursday

8 Friday

REMINDERS

Saturday 9

Sunday 10

BALSAMIC PORK WITH APPLES

Balsamic vinegar 100ml (3½fl oz)
Runny honey 2 tsp
Chopped thyme leaves 2 tsp or 1tsp dried thyme
Pork loin steaks medallions 4, fat removed
Unsalted butter 15g (½oz)
Vegetable oil 1 tsp
Red onions 2 small, peeled and cut into 8 wedges
Red eating apples 2, cored and each cut into thin wedges

1 In a shallow dish, mix together vinegar, honey and herbs, and season to taste. Add pork and turn to coat. Cover and set aside.
2 Meanwhile, heat butter and oil in a large nonstick frying pan. Add onions and cook for 2-3 minutes, stirring occasionally. Add apples and cook for 2 minutes until onions and apples are starting to caramelise. Remove from pan.
3 Drain pork and reserve the marinade. Fry pork for 4-5 minutes over a medium heat, turn over and add onions, apples and reserved marinade. Continue to cook for a further 4-5 minutes or until pork juices run clear.
4 Divide pork between serving plates, and serve with the sauce, onions, apples and seasonal vegetables.

Serves 4 • Time 25 mins
Calories 257 • Fibre 2.2g • Salt 0.9g • Sugar 5.7g
Fat 11g of which 3.9g is saturated

11 Monday

12 Tuesday

13 Wednesday

14 Thursday

15 Friday

● New moon

REMINDERS

Saturday 16

Sunday 17

ORZO WITH MOULES

Dry white wine 150ml (¼ pint)
Fish stock 600ml (1 pint)
Live mussels 900g (2lb), cleaned
Olive oil 2 tbsp
Shallots 4, peeled and finely chopped
Garlic 4 cloves, peeled and finely chopped
Orzo pasta 300g (11oz)
Single cream 4 tbsp
Chopped fresh parsley 4 tbsp

1 Pour wine and stock into a large pan. Bring to the boil, add mussels, cover with a tight-fitting lid and cook over a medium heat, shaking pan occasionally, for about 5 minutes until mussels have opened. Discard any that do not open. Drain, reserving cooking liquid, then cover and keep warm.

2 Heat oil in the same pan and gently fry shallots and garlic for 10 minutes until softened but not browned. Stir in orzo and mix well. Add reserved cooking liquid a ladleful at a time, cooking and stirring until all liquid has been absorbed before adding the next. This will take about 20 minutes. Add more stock or boiling water if pasta is still firm.

3 When orzo is tender, season with pepper and stir in cream. Return mussels to the pan and gently stir into the pasta for 2-3 minutes until piping hot. Serve immediately, sprinkled with chopped parsley.

Serves 4 • Time 50 mins
Calories 543 • Fibre 4.9g • Salt 3g • Sugar 0g
Fat 14.3g of which 3.7g is saturated

18 Monday

19 Tuesday

20 Wednesday

21 Thursday

22 Friday
) First quarter

REMINDERS

Saturday 23
Autumnal equinox
Autumn begins

Sunday 24

Win a year of gorgeous, ethically sourced flowers delivered to your door every month courtesy of Arena Flowers.

This seasonal flower subscription is perfect to brighten your home or give as a gift to your loved ones. Each box will arrive with one or two types of beautiful, fresh seasonal stems and complementary greenery to create a stunning bouquet.

All Arena flowers are sourced from ethical suppliers and Fairtrade-certified farms, and for every order they receive they plant two trees in countries facing deforestation.

Shop online at arenaflowers.com

Enter at **dairydiary.co.uk/win2023**
Or send in your name and address to:
Dairy Diary Competition
PO Box 482, CREWE, CW1 9FG
Closing date 30 November 2023

You can order your 2024 Dairy Diary via your milkman (see p170), or direct from the publisher at dairydiary.co.uk or by phoning 0344 4725265.

25 Monday

26 Tuesday

27 Wednesday

28 Thursday

29 Friday

○ Full moon

REMINDERS

Saturday 30

OCTOBER Sunday 1

VENISON WITH MUSHROOM & BLACKBERRY SAUCE

Venison steaks 4 x 125g (4oz) each
Olive oil 2 tbsp
Red onion 1 small, peeled and thinly sliced
Chestnut mushrooms 200g (7oz), sliced
Fresh thyme a few sprigs
Blackberries 150g (5oz)
Ruby port 3 tbsp
Blackberry or raspberry vinegar 3 tbsp
Bramble or redcurrant jelly 2 tbsp
Mashed potatoes and green vegetables to serve (optional)

1 Season venison on both sides; set aside. Heat 1 tbsp oil in a frying pan and gently fry onion, mushrooms and thyme for 10 minutes.
2 Stir in blackberries, port, vinegar and jelly, bring to the boil, cover and simmer gently for 5 minutes until softened. Turn off the heat. Keep covered.
3 Meanwhile, heat remaining oil in another frying pan until hot. Add steaks and cook over a medium heat for 4 minutes on each side – this will cook them to rare. Pour over hot blackberry sauce, cover and cook over a low heat for a further 5 minutes.
4 Discard thyme sprigs and serve steaks with mashed potatoes and green vegetables, if you like.
TIP This sauce also works well with beef, duck, pheasant and pork – simply adjust the cooking times accordingly.

Serves 4 • Time 35 mins
Calories 247 • Fibre 2.5g • Salt 0.8g • Sugar 6.9g
Fat 7.7g of which 1.8g is saturated

2 Monday

3 Tuesday

4 Wednesday

5 Thursday

6 Friday
☾ Last quarter

REMINDERS

Saturday 7

Sunday 8

GLUTEN-FREE PEANUT BUTTER BROWNIES

Dark chocolate 175g (6oz), broken into pieces
Unsalted butter 100g (3½oz)
Smooth peanut butter 100g (3½oz)
Eggs 2 large, beaten
Light brown soft sugar 110g (4oz)
Cornflour 25g (1oz)
Cocoa powder 2 tbsp
Salt ½ tsp
Vanilla extract 1 tsp
Clear honey 1 tbsp

1 Preheat oven to 180°C/160°fan/Gas 4. Grease and line a 20cm (8in) square cake tin with a double layer of baking paper so it overhangs the tin. Put chocolate, butter and 25g (1oz) peanut butter in a saucepan and melt over a very low heat until blended together, then mix well and cool for 10 minutes.
2 Whisk eggs and sugar in a large bowl for 3-4 minutes until thick and creamy. Sift cornflour and cocoa on top, add melted chocolate mixture, salt and vanilla, and gently stir all ingredients to a thick, smooth batter.
3 Pour into lined tin and smooth top. Blend remaining peanut butter with honey and spoon dollops on top, then swirl and marble through chocolate with a skewer.
4 Bake for 25 minutes until the top forms a shiny, papery skin. The middle should be wobbly. Leave to cool in the tin – it will sink.
5 To serve, carefully remove from the tin using the paper and slice into 12 portions. The brownies will keep in an airtight container for 3-4 days and freeze well.
TIP Other nut and seed butters like almond, cashew or tahini will also work in this recipe.

Makes 12 • Time 40 mins plus cooling
Calories 249 • Fibre 1.2g • Salt 0.3g • Sugar 20.6g
Fat 16.2g of which 8.2g is saturated

9 Monday

10 Tuesday

11 Wednesday

12 Thursday

13 Friday

REMINDERS

Saturday 14

● New moon

Sunday 15

ROASTED SWEETCORN & CHILLI SOUP WITH GRUYÈRE & SAGE TOASTIES

Corn on the cobs 4, husks removed
Olive oil 2 tbsp
Smoked paprika ½ tsp
Leek 1, sliced
Garlic 1 clove, crushed
Red chilli 1, finely chopped
Vegetable stock 800ml (1¼ pints)
Sourdough bread 8 slices
Gruyère cheese 75g (3oz), grated
Sage leaves 8, chopped or ½ tsp dried sage
Butter for spreading

1 Preheat oven to 200°C/180°fan/Gas 6. Put corn in a roasting tin and drizzle with 1 tbsp oil. Sprinkle over paprika and seasoning. Roast for 25-30 minutes, turning halfway through.
2 Heat remaining oil in a pan and fry leek, garlic and chilli, reserving 1 tsp chilli, for 4-5 minutes until softened. Slice off roasted corn kernels, reserving 2 tbsp, and add to the pan with the stock. Bring to a simmer and cook for 3-4 minutes. Using a hand blender, whizz mixture to a smooth soup; season.
3 Prepare cheese and sage sandwiches, buttering the outside of each slice. Place in a heated frying pan for 2-3 minutes on each side or until golden.
4 To serve, ladle into bowls and sprinkle with reserved corn kernels and chilli. Serve toasties alongside.
TIP Gruyère cheese is made with animal rennet. Choose a similar vegetarian hard cheese to cater to vegetarians.

Serves 4 • Time 45 mins
Calories 335 • Fibre 5.4g • Salt 2.3g • Sugar 1.3g
Fat 14.8g of which 4.9g is saturated

16 Monday

Don't forget to order your **2024 Dairy Diary**. Use the order form on page 170 or order online.
If you don't have a milkman, call 0344 4725265 or visit www.dairydiary.co.uk

17 Tuesday

18 Wednesday

19 Thursday

20 Friday

REMINDERS

Saturday 21

Sunday 22
) First quarter

KIMCHI CHICKEN BURGER WITH CELERIAC SLAW

Chicken breasts 2, skinned
Kimchi or gochujang paste 1½ tbsp
Olive oil 2 tbsp
Garlic mayonnaise 3 tbsp
Lemon ½, juice only
Celeriac 200g (7oz), grated or julienned
Small courgette 150g (5oz), julienned
Spring onions 2, shredded
Chopped fresh flat-leaf parsley small handful
Brioche buns 2, toasted
Rocket leaves handful

1 Put chicken on a board and, using a rolling pin covered in clingfilm, flatten to an even thickness of 1cm (¼in). Rub over 1 tbsp kimchi or gochujang paste.
2 Heat oil in a frying pan and fry chicken for 3-4 minutes on each side until golden and cooked through. Leave to rest.
3 In a large bowl, mix together mayonnaise, remaining kimchi paste, lemon juice and seasoning. Stir through celeriac, courgette, spring onions and parsley.
4 Spoon celeriac and parsley slaw onto the bottom of each bun, then top with chicken breast and a pile of rocket leaves to serve.

Serves 2 • Time 25 mins
Calories 597 • Fibre 5.8g • Salt 1.3g • Sugar 4g
Fat 35.7g of which 3.5g is saturated

23 Monday

24 Tuesday

25 Wednesday

26 Thursday

27 Friday

REMINDERS

Saturday 28

○ Full moon

Don't forget to put your clocks back 1 hour tonight
(t.b.c. dependent on Government ruling)

Sunday 29

TREACLE SCONES WITH APPLE SAUCE & CLOTTED CREAM

Self-raising flour 350g (12oz), plus extra for dusting
Baking powder 1 tsp
Mixed spice 1 tsp
Golden caster sugar 4 tbsp, plus extra for dusting
Butter 75g (3oz), cubed
Treacle 3 tbsp
Milk 125ml (4fl oz), plus extra for brushing
Apple sauce and clotted cream to serve

1 Preheat the oven to 200°C/180°fan/Gas 6 and grease and line a baking sheet. Put flour, baking powder, spice, sugar and a pinch of salt in a bowl, then rub in butter until crumbs.
2 Thoroughly mix together treacle and milk and add to dry ingredients, kneading to a soft sticky dough. Turn out onto a floured surface and roll out to a 2cm (¾in) thickness. Stamp out eight 8cm x 6cm (about 3in x 2in) rounds, rerolling the dough once. Place on prepared baking sheet. Brush each scone with extra milk and sprinkle with sugar.
3 Put in the oven and bake for 18-20 minutes until risen and golden.
4 While still warm, slice in half and serve with a dollop of apple sauce and clotted cream.

Makes 8 • **Time 35 mins**
Calories 277 • Fibre 1.8g • Salt 0.6g • Sugar 13.4g
Fat 8.6g of which 5.2g is saturated

30 Monday

31 Tuesday
Halloween

1 Wednesday NOVEMBER

2 Thursday

3 Friday

REMINDERS

Saturday 4

Sunday 5
Bonfire Night
(Last quarter

PUMPKIN & CINNAMON CUSTARD TARTLETS

Pumpkin 75g (3oz), grated
Milk 75ml (2½fl oz)
Double cream 75ml (2½fl oz)
Caster sugar 2 tbsp
Cinnamon and nutmeg pinch of each
Egg 1, beaten
Vanilla extract ¼ tsp
Mini tartlet pastry cases 36
Pumpkin seeds 2 tbsp
Icing sugar to dust

1 Place pumpkin, milk, cream, sugar and spices in a small pan and bring to a simmer. Cover and leave for 2-3 minutes until pumpkin is soft. Using a hand blender, whizz to a smooth liquid.
2 Pour beaten egg and vanilla over; mix well.
3 Preheat oven to 180°C/160°fan/Gas 4. Arrange pastry cases on a baking tray, carefully pour in custard and sprinkle pumpkin seeds over.
4 Bake in the oven for 5 minutes until just set. Serve warm with a dusting of icing sugar.
TIP Replace pumpkin with butternut squash, if preferred.

Makes 36 tartlets • Time 20 mins
Calories 72 • Fibre 0.3g • Salt 0g • Sugar 3.8g
Fat 3.8g of which 2.2g is saturated

6 Monday

7 Tuesday

8 Wednesday

9 Thursday

10 Friday

REMINDERS

Saturday 11

Sunday 12
Remembrance Sunday

RED POPPY FLOWER BISCUITS

Butter 110g (4oz)
Caster sugar 75g (3oz)
Plain flour 110g (4oz), plus extra for dusting
Semolina 50g (2oz)
Lemon extract 1 tsp
Red ready to roll icing 175g (6oz)
Black ready to roll icing 50g (2oz)

1 Put butter, sugar, flour, semolina, a pinch of salt, and lemon extract in the bowl of a food processor and whizz to a smooth dough. Cover in clingfilm and chill for 1 hour.
2 Preheat oven to 160°C/140°fan/Gas 3. On a flour-dusted surface, roll out the dough to 1cm (¼in) thick. Stamp out flowers using a 7cm (2¾in) flower cutter. Reroll the dough to make about 18 flowers.
3 Transfer to prepared baking sheets and bake in the oven for 15-20 minutes until lightly golden. Transfer to a wire rack to cool.
4 Using a 6cm flower cutter, stamp out red icing flowers. Wet slightly underneath and secure on top of each biscuit. Roll a small pea-sized piece of black icing and push in the centre. Using a fork, make short indents around each petal.

Makes 18 • Time 40 mins plus chilling
Calories 137 • Fibre 0.3g • Salt 0g • Sugar 16g
Fat 5.2g of which 3.2g is saturated

13 Monday

● New moon

14 Tuesday

15 Wednesday

16 Thursday

17 Friday

REMINDERS

Saturday 18

Sunday 19

CRISPY MUSHROOM KATSU CURRY

Vegetable oil 1 tbsp, plus extra for frying
Echalion shallot 1, peeled and chopped
Garlic 1 clove, peeled and crushed
Carrot 1 small, peeled and grated
Mild curry powder 1 tsp
Plain flour 1 tsp plus 3 tbsp for dusting
Vegetable stock 300ml (½ pint)
Creamed coconut 25g (1oz), chopped
Large flat mushrooms 4, thickly sliced
Egg 1, beaten
Panko breadcrumbs 100g (3½oz)
Jasmine rice 250g microwave pouch
Fresh coriander leaves small handful, to serve (optional)

1 Heat 1 tbsp oil in a pan and fry shallot, garlic, and carrot for 5-7 minutes until softened. Stir in curry powder and heat for 1 min. Add 1 tsp flour and cook for a further 30 seconds. Gradually stir in stock to make a thick sauce. Stir in coconut and bring to a simmer for 3-4 minutes. Remove from heat and use a hand blender to whizz to a smooth sauce; season to taste.
2 Heat 1cm (¼in) oil in a frying pan. Dip mushrooms in seasoned flour, then egg, and lastly panko breadcrumbs. Fry for 2-3 minutes until crisp and golden. Drain oil on kitchen paper.
3 Heat rice according to packet instructions. Serve with breaded mushrooms, sauce and a sprinkling of fresh coriander leaves, if liked.

Serves 2 • **Time 25 mins**
Calories 535 • Fibre 4.8g • Salt 2.4g • Sugar 2.5g
Fat 16.6g of which 5.2g is saturated

20 Monday

☽ First quarter

21 Tuesday

22 Wednesday

23 Thursday

24 Friday

REMINDERS

Saturday 25

Sunday 26
Stir Up Sunday

BAKED HASSELBACK SWEET POTATO PARCELS

Sweet potatoes 2 medium or large
Olive oil 3 tbsp
Feta 100g (3½oz), sliced
Chorizo 8 thin slices
Oregano small handful
Thyme leaves or chopped sage to garnish (optional)

1 Preheat oven to 200°C/180°fan/Gas 6. Place a sweet potato between two wooden spoons on a board. Cut slices at 1cm (¼in) intervals through each sweet potato until the blade meets the wooden spoon. Put on a baking tray and drizzle each with ½ tbsp oil. Bake for 40-45 minutes or until just tender.
2 Evenly slip slices of feta, chorizo and oregano in between the Hasselback slits and season with salt and pepper. Drizzle over remaining oil and return to the oven for a further 10-15 minutes until cheese softens. Serve immediately scattered with a few thyme leaves or chopped sage, if liked.

Serves 2 • Time 1 hr 10 mins
Calories 468 • Fibre 7.2g • Salt 2.2g • Sugar 0g
Fat 27.2g of which 10.9g is saturated

27 Monday
○ Full moon

28 Tuesday

29 Wednesday

30 Thursday
St Andrew's Day

1 Friday DECEMBER

REMINDERS

Saturday 2

Sunday 3
First Sunday in Advent

SPANISH DRIED FIG & ALMOND CAKE

Dried figs 450g (1lb), stalks trimmed
Ground cinnamon ½ tsp
Ground cloves pinch
Brandy 2 tbsp
Flaked almonds 50g (2oz), toasted
Blanched whole almonds 20, toasted
Spanish cheese such as Manchego and biscuits to serve (optional)

1 Place dried figs in a food processor with ground spices and brandy and whizz to a coarse paste. Transfer mixture to a bowl and stir in flaked almonds.
2 Spoon mixture into a foil-lined 15cm x 6cm (6in x 2½in) deep cake tin and, using more foil, cover and flatten the top with your hands.
3 Decorate the top of the cake using the whole toasted almonds, then cover and leave for at least 2 days to firm up.
4 Slice into thin slices and serve alongside your choice of Spanish cheese, such as Manchego, and biscuits, if liked.

Makes 16 slices • Time 15 mins plus 2 days resting
Calories 106 • Fibre 2.8g • Salt 0g • Sugar 0g
Fat 3.9g of which 0.3g is saturated

4 Monday

5 Tuesday
☾ Last quarter

6 Wednesday

7 Thursday

8 Friday

REMINDERS

Saturday 9

Sunday 10

MINTY SNOWFLAKE MARSHMALLOWS

Icing sugar for dusting
Gelatine leaves 8, halved
Cold mint tea 250ml (9fl oz)
Liquid glucose 140g (4¾oz)
Caster sugar 400g (14oz)
Blue food colouring a few drops

1 Line the base and sides of a 32cm x 22cm (13in x 8½in) baking tray with baking paper and liberally dust with icing sugar.
2 Put gelatine and mint tea in the large bowl of a food mixer and leave to soak.
3 Meanwhile, mix glucose, sugar and a pinch of salt in a pan. Slowly bring to the boil, stirring occasionally and leave to simmer until it reaches 130°C/54°F on a thermometer.
4 Carefully pour into tea gel and whisk using an electric whisk on high for 10 minutes until thick, white and doubled in size. Put half of mixture into one half of the lined baking tray.
5 Add 2-3 drops of blue food colouring to the remainder and whisk for 30 seconds. Transfer this to the other half of the baking tray, smoothing to an even level. Place uncovered in the fridge and leave to set overnight.
6 Using plenty of icing sugar to dust, stamp out snowflakes using a 7cm (2¾in) cutter. Dust each snowflake with icing sugar again and leave to dry out on a wire rack overnight.

Makes 12 • Time 35 mins plus overnight setting
Calories 181 • Fibre 0g • Salt 0g • Sugar 41g
Fat 0g of which 0g is saturated

11 Monday

12 Tuesday

● New moon

13 Wednesday

14 Thursday

15 Friday

REMINDERS

Saturday 16

Sunday 17

CHRISTMAS SPICED SODA GLAZED HAM

Unsmoked gammon joint 2kg (4lb 6oz)
Onion 1, peeled and chopped
Carrot 1, peeled and sliced
Fresh rosemary 3 sprigs
Bay leaves 2
Cinnamon stick 1
Whole cloves 6, plus extra for studding
Black peppercorns 1 tsp
Regular cola 1.75 litres (3 pints)
Clementines 2, juice of 1, the other sliced
Dijon mustard 2 tsp
Chilli flakes a pinch

1 Put gammon in a large pan with onion, carrot, herbs and spices. Pour over 1½ litres (2½ pints) cola. Bring to a simmer and leave, covered, for 1½ hours.
2 Remove from the liquid and place in a foil-lined roasting tin. Run a knife under the rind to remove and score fat in a diamond pattern.
3 Preheat oven to 200°C/180°fan/Gas 6. Meanwhile, put 250ml (8½fl oz) cola in a pan and bring to the boil. Leave for 12-15 minutes until reduced to a syrupy glaze. Stir in clementine juice, mustard and chilli flakes and brush all over ham. Arrange clementine slices on top, securing with the cloves.
4 Bake for 20-25 minutes, basting a couple of times, until nicely glazed.

Serves 8 • Time 2 hrs
Calories 381 • Fibre 0.8g • Salt 5.6g • Sugar 8.2g
Fat 19g of which 6.3g is saturated

18 Monday

19 Tuesday

☽ First quarter

20 Wednesday

21 Thursday

22 Friday

Winter solstice
Winter begins

REMINDERS

Saturday 23

Sunday 24
Christmas Eve

MULLED WINE JELLY TRIFLES

Mandarin oranges 312g tin in light syrup
Caster sugar 25g (1oz)
Cinnamon stick 1, broken
Cloves 6
Leaf gelatine 3 sheets
Fruity red wine 300ml (½ pint)
Madeira cake 110g (4oz), cubed
Vanilla custard 200ml (7fl oz)
Whipping cream 150ml (¼ pint)
Ground cinnamon to dust

1 Drain mandarin syrup from tin into a small saucepan. Add sugar and spices. Heat gently until sugar dissolves, bring to the boil and simmer gently for 3 minutes. Set aside.
2 Meanwhile, soak gelatine sheets in cold water for 5 minutes. Drain well and add to hot syrup. Stir until dissolved then mix in wine. Leave to cool; discard the spices.
3 Reserving a few mandarins for decoration, layer remainder with cake in 4 tall sundae or coffee glasses and gently pour over the cold jelly mix. Chill for 2 hours or until ready to serve.
4 To serve, top each trifle with custard. Whip cream until just peaking and spoon on top. Dust with cinnamon and decorate with reserved mandarins.
TIPS Canned pears in natural juice would make a good fruity substitute in this recipe. If you prefer not to use wine, replace with grape juice or use fresh orange juice for an extra kick of citrus.

Serves 4 • Time 20 mins plus cooling & chilling
Calories 415 • Fibre 0.3g • Salt 0.4g • Sugar 30.2g
Fat 20.7g of which 12.7g is saturated

25 Monday
Christmas Day
Bank Holiday, UK

26 Tuesday
Boxing Day
Bank Holiday, UK

27 Wednesday
○ Full moon

28 Thursday

29 Friday

REMINDERS

Saturday 30

Sunday 31
New Year's Eve

PICKLED PEAR & CRISPY TURKEY SALAD WITH BLUE CHEESE DRESSING

Cider vinegar 3 tbsp
Maple syrup 1 tbsp
Red onion 1 small, sliced
Pear 1, peeled and sliced
Olive oil 1 tbsp
Leftover cooked turkey 150g (5oz), roughly sliced
Mixed salad leaves 2 large handfuls
Blue cheese such as Stilton 25g (1oz), crumbled
Milk 3-4 tbsp
Walnuts 25g (1oz), chopped

1 In a large bowl mix together vinegar, maple syrup and seasoning. Toss through onion and pear; set aside.
2 Heat oil in a frying pan and fry turkey for 3-4 minutes until crispy and golden.
3 Mix salad leaves through onion and pear to coat in the pickling liquid. Spoon onto plates, keeping any remaining juices in the bowl. Mix in blue cheese and enough milk to whisk to a smooth dressing.
4 Top salad with the crispy turkey, chopped walnuts and the blue cheese dressing.

Serves 2 • Time 10 mins
Calories 400 • Fibre 3.9g • Salt 0.4g • Sugar 6g
Fat 20.8g of which 5.6g is saturated

1 Monday

New Year's Day
Bank Holiday, UK

2 Tuesday

Bank Holiday, Scotland

3 Wednesday

4 Thursday

(Last quarter

5 Friday

REMINDERS

NOTES

NOTES

NOTES

NOTES

NOTES

NOTES

Three ways to order your Dairy Diary

FROM YOUR MILKMAN

Use the **order form overleaf**, or, if you usually order via your dairy's website, please order online.

TELEPHONE

If you do not have a milkman, call **0344 4725265.** Your diary will be posted to you.

ONLINE

Visit **dairydiary.co.uk**
See full details of the 2024 Dairy Diary and other great products.

DISCOVER MORE RECIPES & FABULOUS COMPETITIONS

Visit **dairydiary.co.uk**
Follow us on **Instagram** @originaldairydiary
Like us on **Facebook** @dairydiary

Reserve your Dairy Diary 2024

To reserve your copy of the 2024 Dairy Diary, please fill in the form overleaf and leave it out with your empties from September onwards.

If you usually order via your dairy's website, please order online.

Order form overleaf...

Dairy Diary 2024

Order form

MILKMAN PLEASE LEAVE ME

☐ copies of the **Dairy Diary 2024**

☐ copies of the **Dairy Diary Set**

Name ______________________

Address ______________________

____

____

____

Postcode ______________________

THANK YOU

Please leave out for your milkman from September 2023 onwards

RECIPE NOTES

- Nutritional information has been calculated by portion or item. Where there are portion variations, e.g. serves 6–8, the analysis given is based on the larger number.
- Spoon measures are level unless otherwise stated.
- Eggs are large unless otherwise stated.
- Sugar is 'free sugars' (added sugars, including those naturally present in fruit juice, honey & syrups, but excluding the natural sugars present in all fruit and vegetables).
- Recipes that do not contain animal products (such as meat, fish, poultry, dairy, eggs and honey) are suitable for vegans. Please check ingredients carefully for dietary suitability.

SAFETY NOTES

- Recipes using nuts or nut products are not suitable for young children or those with a nut allergy.
- Certain at-risk groups, such as pregnant women, babies and sick or elderly people should not eat raw or lightly cooked eggs.

(V) Suitable for vegetarians, provided a suitable cheese, yogurt or pesto etc. is used.

(V) Suitable for vegans provided the non-dairy options are chosen, and no honey is added.

(F) Suitable for freezing.

Soup, Starters, Salads, Sides & Snacks

Main Courses

Desserts & Puddings

Cakes & Bakes

Drinks

Miscellaneous

THERE ARE LOTS MORE RECIPES AT
DAIRYDIARY.CO.UK

PLANNER 2024

JANUARY	FEBRUARY	MARCH
1 Mon BANK HOLIDAY UK	1 Thu	1 Fri
2 Tue BANK HOLIDAY SCOTLAND	2 Fri	**2 Sat**
3 Wed	**3 Sat**	**3 Sun**
4 Thu	**4 Sun**	4 Mon
5 Fri	5 Mon	5 Tue
6 Sat	6 Tue	6 Wed
7 Sun	7 Wed	7 Thu
8 Mon	8 Thu	8 Fri
9 Tue	9 Fri	**9 Sat**
10 Wed	**10 Sat**	**10 Sun**
11 Thu	**11 Sun**	11 Mon
12 Fri	12 Mon	12 Tue
13 Sat	13 Tue	13 Wed
14 Sun	14 Wed	14 Thu
15 Mon	15 Thu	15 Fri
16 Tue	16 Fri	**16 Sat**
17 Wed	**17 Sat**	**17 Sun**
18 Thu	**18 Sun**	18 Mon BANK HOLIDAY N. IRELAND
19 Fri	19 Mon	19 Tue
20 Sat	20 Tue	20 Wed
21 Sun	21 Wed	21 Thu
22 Mon	22 Thu	22 Fri
23 Tue	23 Fri	**23 Sat**
24 Wed	**24 Sat**	**24 Sun**
25 Thu	**25 Sun**	25 Mon
26 Fri	26 Mon	26 Tue
27 Sat	27 Tue	27 Wed
28 Sun	28 Wed	28 Thu
29 Mon	29 Thu	29 Fri BANK HOLIDAY UK
30 Tue		**30 Sat**
31 Wed		**31 Sun**

APRIL		MAY		JUNE	
1 Mon	BANK HOLIDAY UK (EXCL. SCOTLAND)	1 Wed		**1 Sat**	
2 Tue		2 Thu		**2 Sun**	
3 Wed		3 Fri		3 Mon	
4 Thu		**4 Sat**		4 Tue	
5 Fri		**5 Sun**		5 Wed	
6 Sat		6 Mon	BANK HOLIDAY UK	6 Thu	
7 Sun		7 Tue		7 Fri	
8 Mon		8 Wed		**8 Sat**	
9 Tue		9 Thu		**9 Sun**	
10 Wed		10 Fri		10 Mon	
11 Thu		**11 Sat**		11 Tue	
12 Fri		**12 Sun**		12 Wed	
13 Sat		13 Mon		13 Thu	
14 Sun		14 Tue		14 Fri	
15 Mon		15 Wed		**15 Sat**	
16 Tue		16 Thu		**16 Sun**	
17 Wed		17 Fri		17 Mon	
18 Thu		**18 Sat**		18 Tue	
19 Fri		**19 Sun**		19 Wed	
20 Sat		20 Mon		20 Thu	
21 Sun		21 Tue		21 Fri	
22 Mon		22 Wed		**22 Sat**	
23 Tue		23 Thu		**23 Sun**	
24 Wed		24 Fri		24 Mon	
25 Thu		**25 Sat**		25 Tue	
26 Fri		**26 Sun**		26 Wed	
27 Sat		27 Mon	BANK HOLIDAY UK	27 Thu	
28 Sun		28 Tue		28 Fri	
29 Mon		29 Wed		**29 Sat**	
30 Tue		30 Thu		**30 Sun**	
		31 Fri			

P.T.O. July–December 2024

JULY		AUGUST		SEPTEMBER	
1	Mon	1	Thu	**1**	**Sun**
2	Tue	2	Fri	2	Mon
3	Wed	**3**	**Sat**	3	Tue
4	Thu	**4**	**Sun**	4	Wed
5	Fri	5	Mon BANK HOLIDAY SCOTLAND	5	Thu
6	**Sat**	6	Tue	6	Fri
7	**Sun**	7	Wed	**7**	**Sat**
8	Mon	8	Thu	**8**	**Sun**
9	Tue	9	Fri	9	Mon
10	Wed	**10**	**Sat**	10	Tue
11	Thu	**11**	**Sun**	11	Wed
12	Fri BANK HOLIDAY N. IRELAND	12	Mon	12	Thu
13	**Sat**	13	Tue	13	Fri
14	**Sun**	14	Wed	**14**	**Sat**
15	Mon	15	Thu	**15**	**Sun**
16	Tue	16	Fri	16	Mon
17	Wed	**17**	**Sat**	17	Tue
18	Thu	**18**	**Sun**	18	Wed
19	Fri	19	Mon	19	Thu
20	**Sat**	20	Tue	20	Fri
21	**Sun**	21	Wed	**21**	**Sat**
22	Mon	22	Thu	**22**	**Sun**
23	Tue	23	Fri	23	Mon
24	Wed	**24**	**Sat**	24	Tue
25	Thu	**25**	**Sun**	25	Wed
26	Fri	26	Mon BANK HOLIDAY UK (EXCL. SCOTLAND)	26	Thu
27	**Sat**	27	Tue	27	Fri
28	**Sun**	28	Wed	**28**	**Sat**
29	Mon	29	Thu	**29**	**Sun**
30	Tue	30	Fri	30	Mon
31	Wed	**31**	**Sat**		

OCTOBER	NOVEMBER	DECEMBER
1 Tue	1 Fri	**1 Sun**
2 Wed	**2 Sat**	2 Mon
3 Thu	**3 Sun**	3 Tue
4 Fri	4 Mon	4 Wed
5 Sat	5 Tue	5 Thu
6 Sun	6 Wed	6 Fri
7 Mon	7 Thu	**7 Sat**
8 Tue	8 Fri	**8 Sun**
9 Wed	**9 Sat**	9 Mon
10 Thu	**10 Sun**	10 Tue
11 Fri	11 Mon	11 Wed
12 Sat	12 Tue	12 Thu
13 Sun	13 Wed	13 Fri
14 Mon	14 Thu	**14 Sat**
15 Tue	15 Fri	**15 Sun**
16 Wed	**16 Sat**	16 Mon
17 Thu	**17 Sun**	17 Tue
18 Fri	18 Mon	18 Wed
19 Sat	19 Tue	19 Thu
20 Sun	20 Wed	20 Fri
21 Mon	21 Thu	**21 Sat**
22 Tue	22 Fri	**22 Sun**
23 Wed	**23 Sat**	23 Mon
24 Thu	**24 Sun**	24 Tue
25 Fri	25 Mon	25 Wed BANK HOLIDAY UK
26 Sat	26 Tue	26 Thu BANK HOLIDAY UK
27 Sun	27 Wed	27 Fri
28 Mon	28 Thu	**28 Sat**
29 Tue	29 Fri	**29 Sun**
30 Wed	**30 Sat**	30 Mon
31 Thu		31 Tue

ACKNOWLEDGEMENTS

Managing Editor
Emily Davenport

Author/Editor
Louise Burfitt

Art Editor
Graham Meigh

Production
Siobhan Hennessey

Recipes
Kathryn Hawkins
Clare Lewis

Photographer
Steve Lee

Food Stylist
Sian Davies

Props Stylist
Agathe Gits

Recipe Testing
Lucy Goodman
Katy Hackforth
Laura Pickering
Gudrun Waskett

Nutritional Analysis
Paul McArdle

Proofreader
Aune Butt

Marketing Executive
Katy Hackforth

Special Thanks
Izzie Cox (Pam Lloyd)
Denise Spencer-Walker (AHDB)
Heidi Wilkins (Letsknit.co.uk)

Published by Eaglemoss Ltd

Dairy Diary, PO Box 482, Crewe, CW1 9FG

Dairy Diary orders telephone: 0344 4725265

Editorial queries telephone: 01270 270050

Website: dairydiary.co.uk   Facebook: @DairyDiary   Instagram: @OriginalDairyDiary

Email: enquiries@dairydiary.co.uk

PICTURE CREDITS

Cover Shutterstock/zolochevka; 21 Shutterstock/Hannamariah; 22 Shutterstock/Tartila; 23 Dreamstime/Wirestock; 23 Shutterstock/Andy Tam; 26 Let's Knit; 28 Shutterstock/Korke; 30 Shutterstock/Whyframe; 31 Shutterstock/Jacob Lund; 32 Shutterstock/Vitalii Matokha; 34 Dreamstime/Pavelvasenkov; 35 Shutterstock/PJ photography; 36 Shutterstock/HelloRF Zcool; 37 Shutterstock/Chris E Mitchell; 38 Shutterstock/Gardens by Design; 39 Shutterstock/Sergey V Kalyakin; 41 Shutterstock/Arjuna Kodisinghe; 42 Shutterstock/Madeleine Steinbach; 45 Shutterstock/Bondar Illia; 45 Shutterstock/istetiana; 46 Shutterstock/Africa Studio; 50 Shutterstock/CWA Studios; 53–159 Eaglemoss/Steve Lee except 73, 105 and 127 AHDB (Agriculture, Horticulture Development Board); 81 BritishAsparagus.com.